FINDING PLACES ON A MODEL OF EARTH

Use the picture to complete the riddles below. For help, you can look back at pages G4–G11 in your textbook.

W9-CCB-231

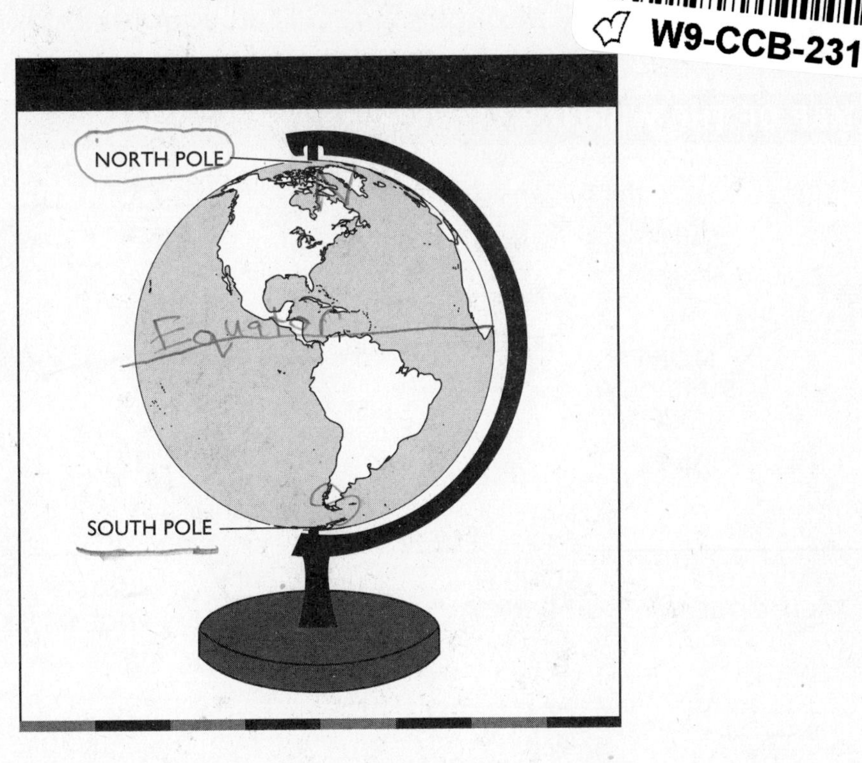

1. Look at my picture above. I am a small model of Earth.

   What am I? globe ______________

2. I am the farthest place north on Earth. What am I?
   Circle my name on the globe above.

3. I am the farthest place south on Earth. What am I?
   Underline my name on the globe.

4. I am an imaginary line circling Earth.
   I am halfway between the North Pole and the South Pole.
   Draw me on the globe. Then label me.

5. I live on the northern half of Earth.
   Put an **N** on the part of Earth where I live.

6. I live on the southern half of Earth.
   Put an **S** on that part of Earth.

PROPERTY OF BD. OF EDUCATION
CITY OF NEW YORK
NYSTL PROGRAM

Where in the World?

Dana took a trip around the world. Connect the numbers on the map to see the route she took. Then complete the activities below. For help, you can look back at pages G4–G11 in your textbook.

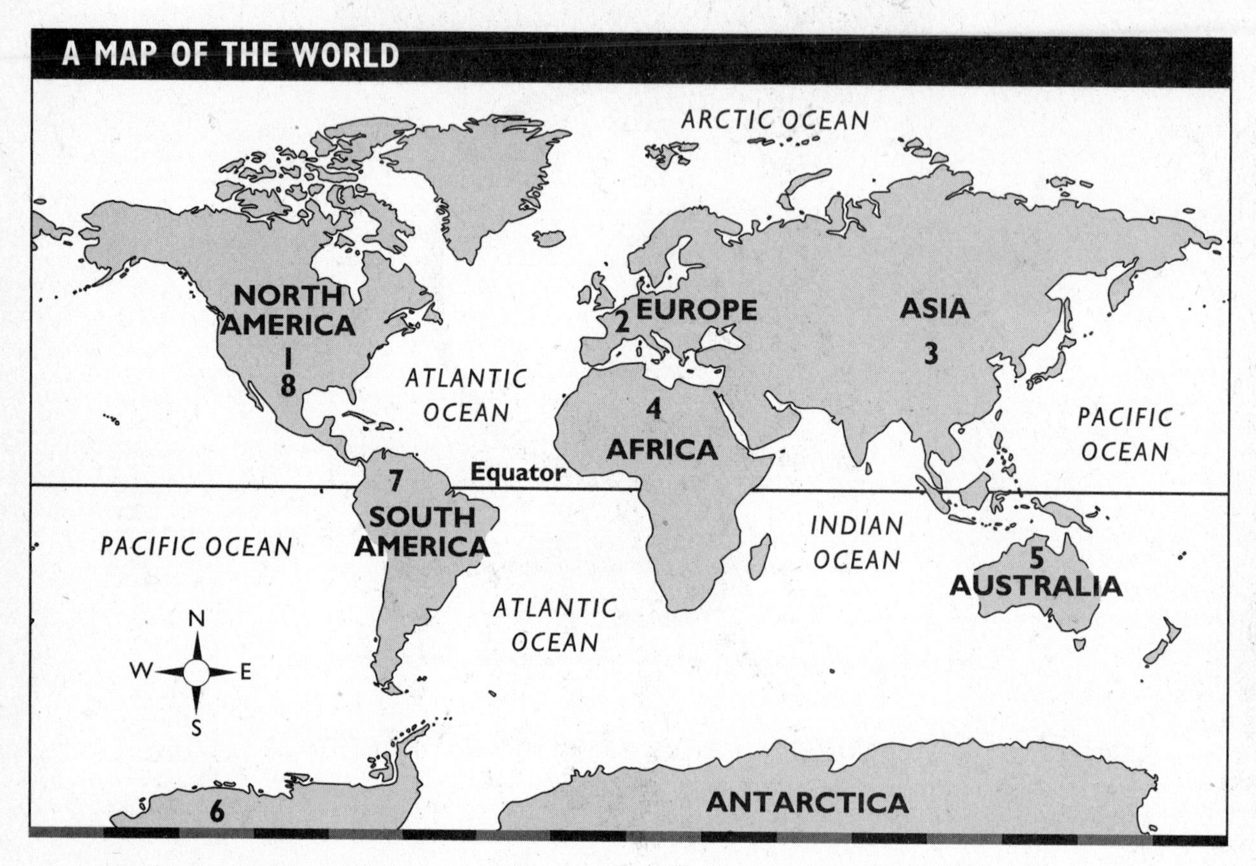

1. Where did Dana begin and end her trip? North Amica

2. Write the name of the continent Dana visited at each stop.

Stop 2: Europe
Stop 3: Asia
Stop 4: Africa
Stop 5: Austratia
Stop 6: Antarctica
Stop 7: South Amrioa

3. Write the name of the ocean Dana flew over between stops.

Between Stop 1 and Stop 2: Alantic
Between Stop 4 and Stop 5: Indian
Between Stop 6 and Stop 7: pacific

USING A MAP AND MAP KEY

Suppose you are visiting a friend who lives in the community shown on the map below. Use the map and the map key to complete the activities. For help, look at pages G4–G11 in your textbook.

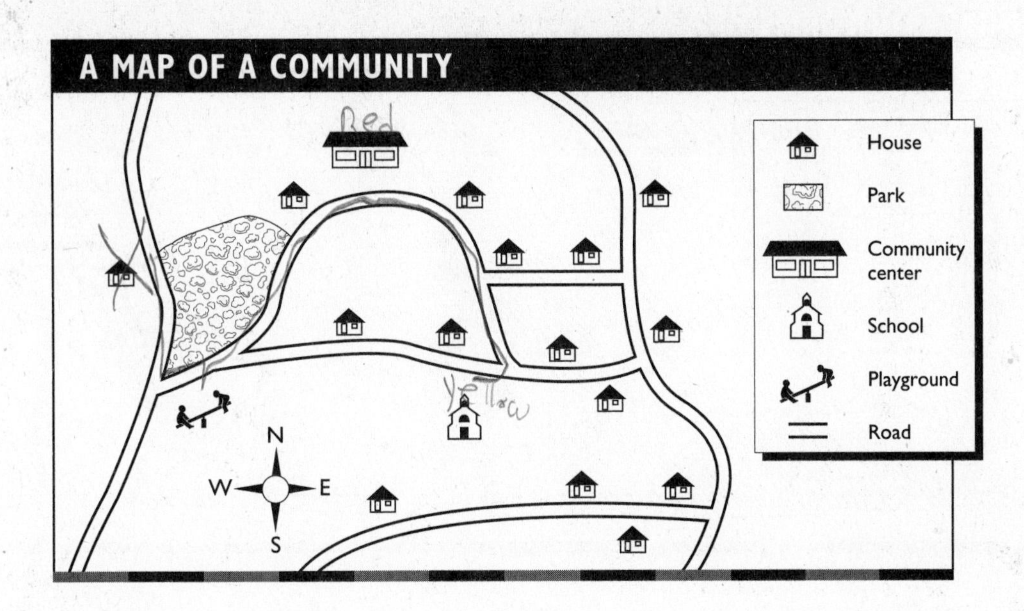

1. Your friend lives next to the park. What symbol shows the park? Circle your answer.

2. Your friend's house is west of the park. Put an **X** on the house.

3. You and your friend walk to the playground. What symbol shows the playground? Circle your answer.

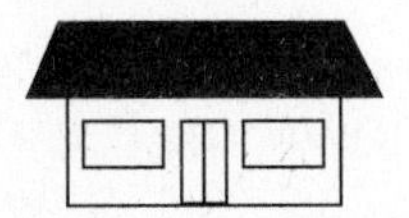 

4. Next you and your friend decide to visit the community center. Find the community center on the map. Color it red.

5. Now your friend wants to show you the school. Find the school on the map. Color it yellow.

6. Draw a line along the road to show the route you and your friend took on your walk through the neighborhood. For help, read the questions again.

Name: Use with pages G4–G11.

Using a Landform Map

Use the map on this page to complete the activities below. For help, you can look back at pages G4–G11 in your textbook.

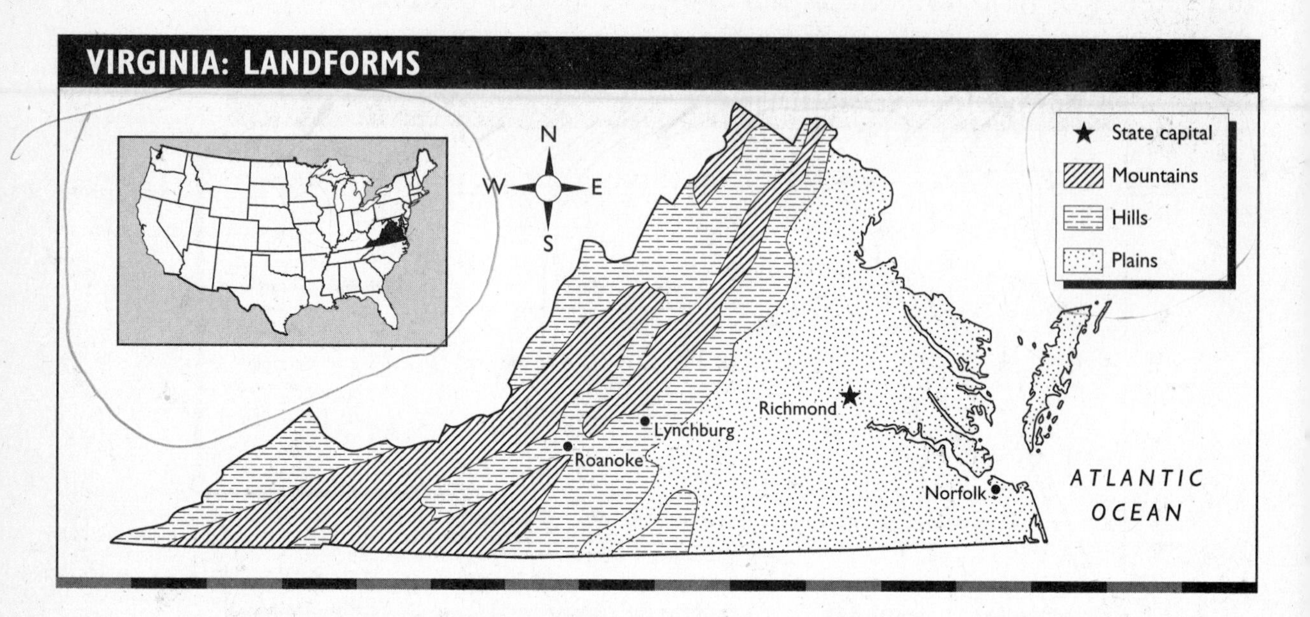

1. Look at the map title. What does the map show?

Virginia Landforms

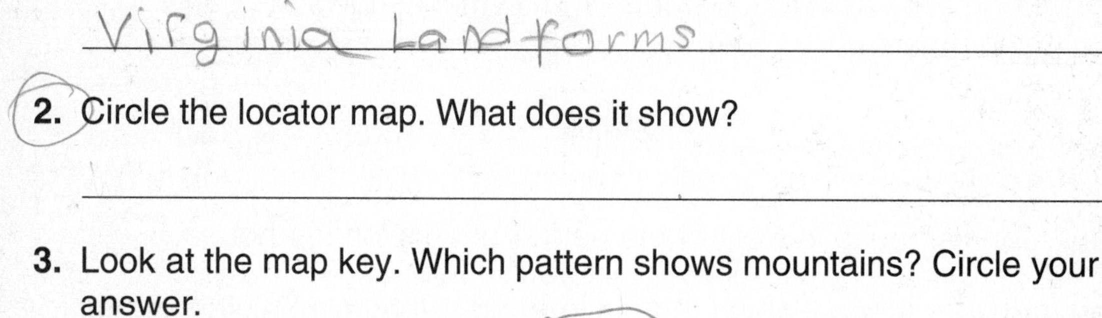

2. Circle the locator map. What does it show?

3. Look at the map key. Which pattern shows mountains? Circle your answer.

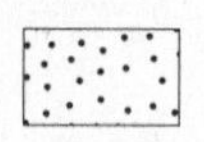

4. What other landforms are shown on the map?

hills and plains

5. Locate Virginia's state capital. On what kind of landform is it located?

plains

6. Find the city of Lynchburg, west of the state capital. On what kind of landform is Lynchburg located? hills and plains

Finding Places on a Grid

The map below shows Central Park in New York City. Look at the map. Then circle the correct answer to each question. For help, you can look back at pages G4–G11 in your textbook.

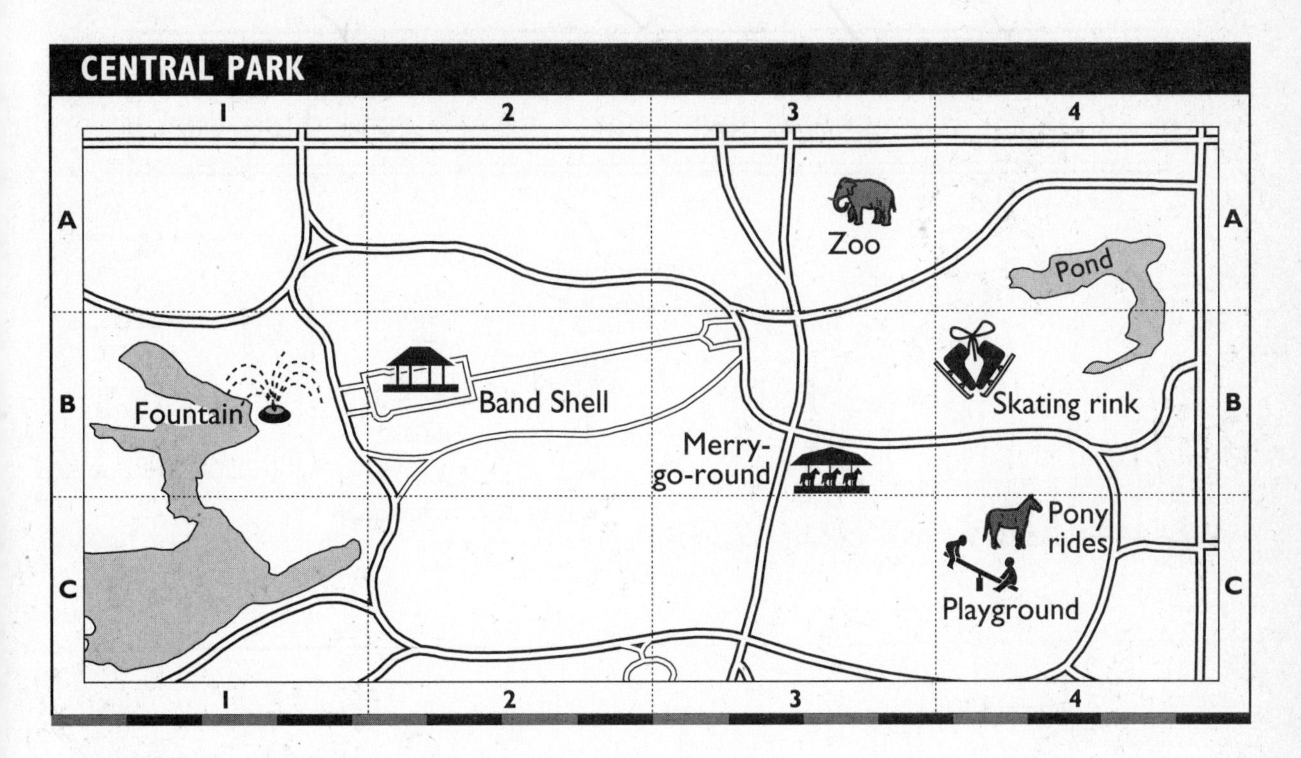

1. Marcia and her friends wanted to visit the zoo. In which square is the zoo located?

   A3 A2 B3 C4

2. After visiting the zoo, Marcia and her friends went to the playground. In which square is the playground located?

   B3 A4 C4 B2

3. Marcia wanted to show her friends something in square B3. What did she want to show them?

   a fountain a merry-go-round a skating rink

4. Marcia and her friends went to square B1. What did they see there?

   a pond a band shell a fountain

Looking at a Community

The pictures show some things that make up a community. Write the word or words from the box that describe each picture. For help, you can look back at pages 8–13 in your book.

people	neighborhood	people helping
stores	people having fun	people working together

Different Kinds of Communities

Read what each person says. Then draw a line to the picture that shows the person's community. For help, you can look back at pages 16–21 in your book.

I live in a farming community. There are few stores nearby, but there is a lot of open land. People need cars to get around.

urban community

I live in a very large city. Many people live in apartment buildings. My city has many stores, restaurants, and tall office buildings.

suburban community

I live in a community near a large city. Most people here live in houses near each other. There are business areas where people work.

rural community

Write a sentence that describes your community. There are houses for people to live in.

Using a Map Scale

Use the map and the map scale to answer the questions. For help, you can look back at pages 22–23 in your book.

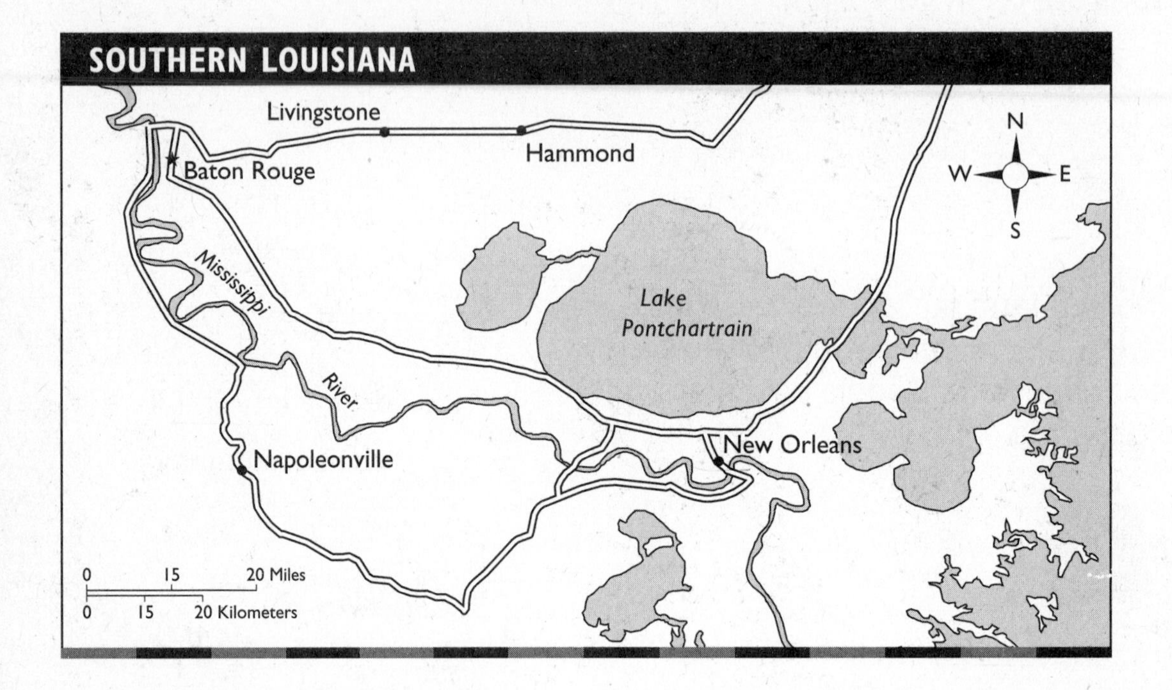

1. Ed's family is going to drive from New Orleans to Baton Rouge. About how far will they travel?

   60 miles

2. Cathy's family is driving from New Orleans to Napoleonville. About how far will they travel?

   40 miles

3. Whose trip is longer, Ed's or Cathy's?

   Ed's

4. How does the map scale help you know this?

   It helps me mesure how many miles.

5. Cathy wants to see the Mississippi River while she is in Napoleonville. About how far will she have to travel?

   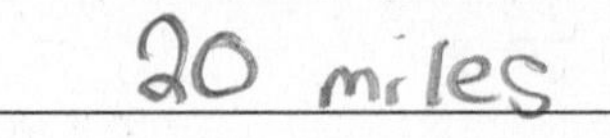

6. Rob lives in Baton Rouge. He wants to take a driving trip. But he does not want to travel more than 40 miles from home. Which city on the map can he visit?

   Napoleonville

7. About how far away is this city from Baton Rouge?

   40 miles

Name: Use with pages 24–29.

Thinking About Mexico City

Use this picture of El Zócalo to help you complete the activities below. For help, you can look back at pages 24–29 in your book.

1. List two ways Mexico City is different from most urban communities in the United States.

They speak spanish. It is a small

controyy.

Circle the word or words that best describe the reason for these differences.

size age culture

2. List two ways Mexico City is like many urban communities in the United States.

3. List two ways Cuajimalpa, Mexico, and Bothell, Washington, are alike.

USING NEW WORDS

Choose a word or words from the box to complete each sentence.
For help, you can refer to the lessons in Chapter 1 of your book.

port	suburb	transportation	culture
rural	hurricane	national park	citizen
urban	pollution	community	island

1. A storm with very strong winds and heavy rains is a hurricane.
2. A member of a community or a country is a Citizen.
3. Anything that spoils land, water, or air is called pollution.
4. A place made up of several neighborhoods where people live, work, and have fun together is a community.
5. A place where ships load and unload goods is called a Port.
6. Land surrounded on all sides by water is called an island.
7. A place of farms and open country is rural.
8. A community that includes a city and its surrounding areas is called an suburban community.
9. Moving people and products from place to place is called transportation.
10. Land set aside by a government for all people to enjoy is a culture.
11. A community located near a city is a urban.
12. The way of life of a group of people is its national park.

Name: Use with pages 36–43.

LOOKING AT OUR COUNTRY'S GEOGRAPHY

Use the map to complete the activities on this page. For help, you can look back at pages 36–43 in your book.

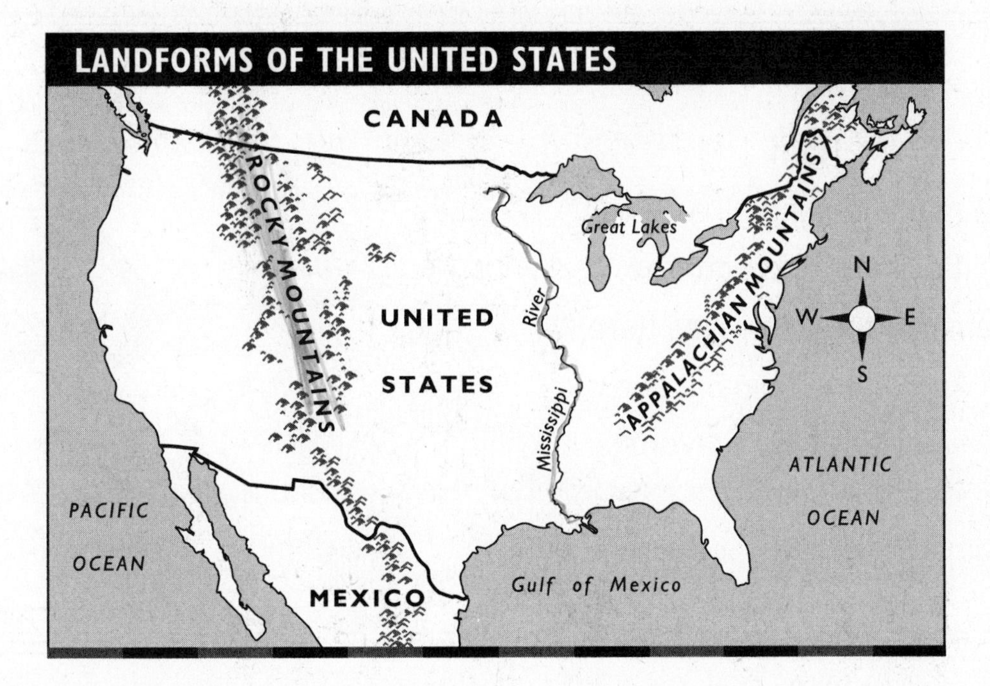

1. What two large bodies of water border the United States?

   ~~Mississippi River~~ ATLantic & pacific

2. What large landform extends from the western part of the United States north into Canada?

   rocky mountins.

3. Find this landform on the map. Color it brown.

4. What body of water lets boats travel from the middle of the United States south to the Gulf of Mexico?

   missisSipPi river

5. Find this body of water on the map. Trace it in blue.

Name: Use with pages 46–49.

LOOKING AT OUR NATURAL RESOURCES

Read the poem. Then complete the activities below. For help, you can look back at pages 46–49 in your book.

Rain

The rain is raining all around.
It falls on field and tree,
It rains on the umbrellas here,
And on the ships at sea.
–Robert Louis Stevenson

1. Name the natural resource mentioned in the poem. rain

2. Give two reasons this natural resource is important.

plants need rain to grow, rain is made of water and People need water to drink.

3. The poem names one natural resource. In the chart below, three other natural resources are listed. Tell how each resource is used.

NATURAL RESOURCES	USE
trees	give oxagen
air	to breath
soil	for plants

Name: Use with pages 50–51.

USING INTERMEDIATE DIRECTIONS

Use the map to answer the questions. Draw a circle around your answer. For help, you can look back at pages 50–51 in your book.

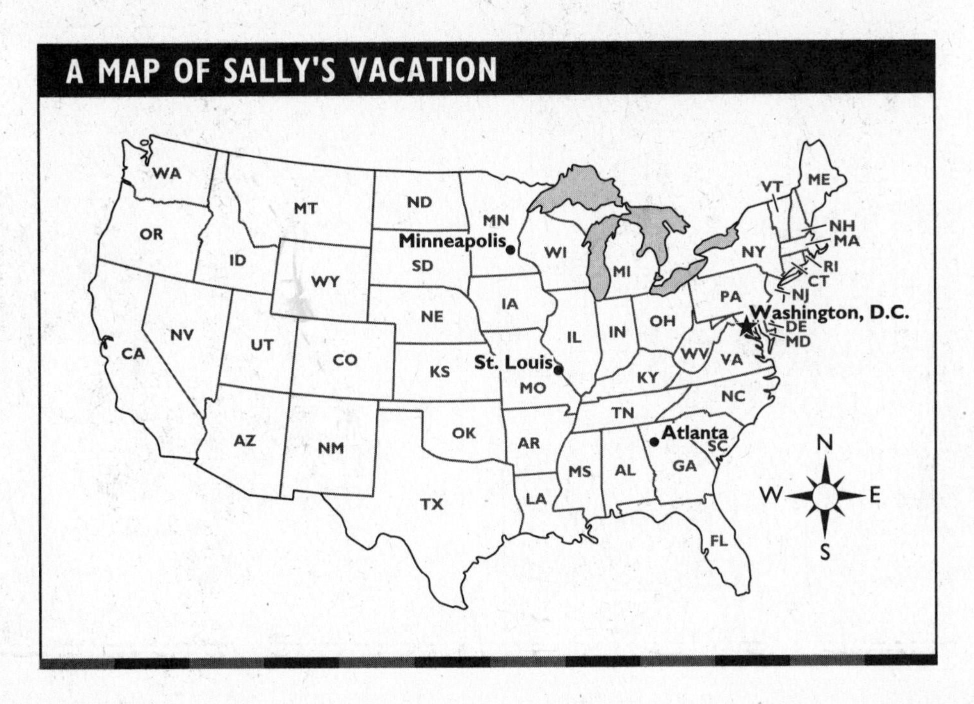

1. Sally's family is taking a vacation. First they are going from St. Louis, Missouri, to Atlanta, Georgia. In what direction will they be going?

   NE **SE** **SW** **NW**

2. Next Sally's family is going from Atlanta to Washington, D.C. What direction will they take?

   NE **SE** **SW** **NW**

3. From Washington, D.C., Sally's family will travel to Minneapolis, Minnesota. In what direction will they be traveling?

   NE **SE** **SW** **NW**

4. From Minneapolis, Sally's family will fly home to St. Louis. In what direction will they be flying?

   NE **SE** **SW** **NW**

Finding Facts About Paracas

Use the pictures to complete the activities below. For help, you can look back at pages 52–56 in your book.

1. Color the picture that shows what Paracas is like.

2. Put an **X** next to each sentence that is true about Paracas.

_____ **a.** Paracas is a rural ocean community in Peru.

_____ **b.** Almost everyone in Paracas makes a living from fishing.

_____ **c.** There are many tall buildings in Paracas.

_____ **d.** The children in Paracas play soccer on the beach.

_____ **e.** Forests are an important natural resource in Paracas.

_____ **f.** People come from all over the world to see the wildlife in Paracas.

_____ **g.** Farming is an important part of life in Paracas.

Hemisphere Detective

Be a hemisphere detective. Use the maps to answer the questions. For help, you can look back at pages 58–59 in your book.

1. I am on a continent. It is completely in the Western Hemisphere. It is also completely in the Northern Hemisphere. Where am I? Color the continent red.

2. I am on a different continent now. Most of this continent is in the Northern Hemisphere and the Eastern Hemisphere. Some of it is in every hemisphere. Where am I? Color the continent green.

3. I am now on a continent that is in the Eastern Hemisphere. Some of it is also in the Southern Hemisphere and in the Northern Hemisphere. Where am I now? Color the continent yellow.

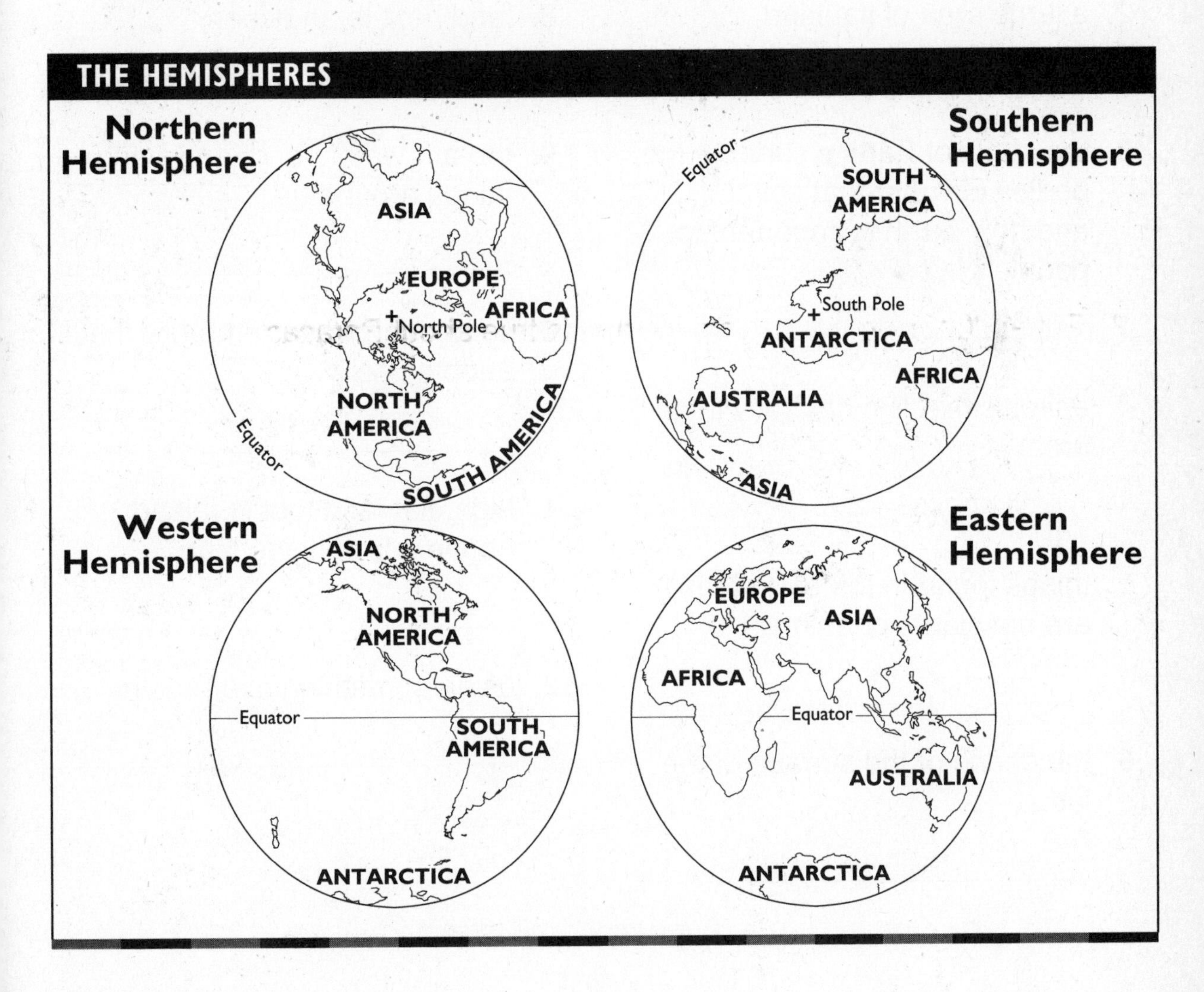

Thinking About New Words

Write each word or pair of words under its meaning. For help, you can refer to the lessons in Chapter 2 of your book.

coast	environment	landform	wildlife
plain	natural resource	geography	minerals
climate	peninsula	recycling	plateau

1. land surrounded by water on three sides

   ______

2. a large area of flat land

   ______

3. the study of Earth's surface, the bodies of water that cover it, and how Earth is important to people's lives

   ______

4. animals that live naturally in an area

   ______

5. things found in the earth that are not plants or animals

   ______

6. the shape of the surface of the land

   ______

7. the weather of a place over a long period of time

   ______

8. land next to an ocean

   ______

9. the air, water, land, and living things around us

   ______

10. something found in nature that people use

    ______

11. high, flat land that is raised above surrounding land

    ______

12. using something over again

    ______

Name: Use with pages 70–75.

LOCATING NATIVE AMERICAN CULTURES

Use the map and pages 70–75 in your book to complete the chart. Name each cultural area and one culture group that lives in each area. The first one has been done for you.

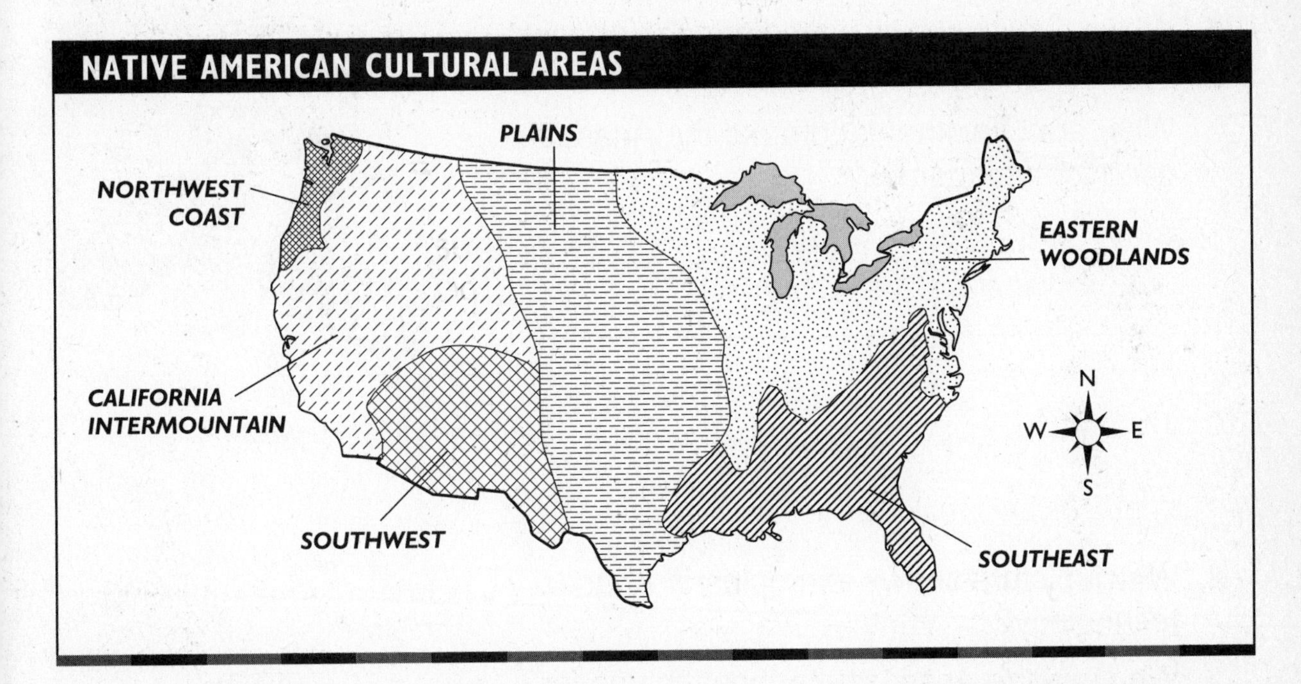

MAP KEY	CULTURAL AREA AND GROUP
	Plains—Blackfoot,

LOOKING AT WHERE THE ANASAZI LIVED

Draw a line from the first question in each group to the picture that answers it. Then write the answer to the second question. For help, you can look back at pages 78–81 in your book.

1. Which picture shows a landform the Anasazi used for their homes?

   What are two other landforms the Anasazi used for their homes?

   ____

   ____

2. Which picture shows examples of Anasazi technology?

   What did the Anasazi use these things for?

   ____

   ____

   ____

3. Which picture shows examples of how the Anasazi used the resources of the desert to make things?

   What natural resources did the Anasazi use to make these things?

   ____

   ____

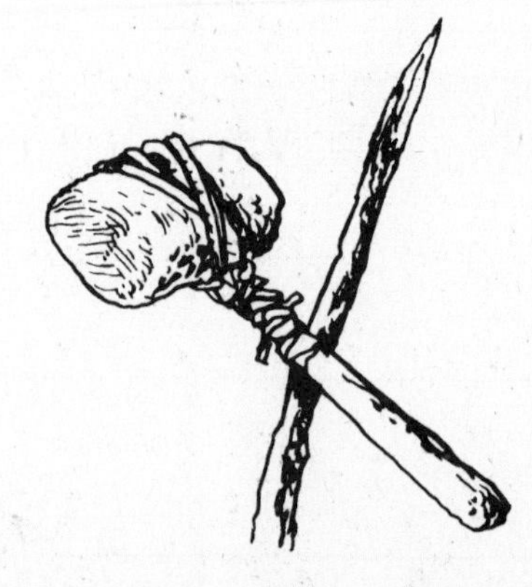

TALKING WITH AN ANASAZI

Suppose you could talk to Little Rabbit at Mesa Verde. Below are some questions you might ask. Think about how he might answer your questions. Write his answers on the lines in complete sentences. For help, you can look back at pages 82–87 in your book.

Question: What kind of house do you live in? How would you describe it?

Answer: ______________________________

____

Question: What jobs do men and women have in your community?

Answer: ______________________________

____

____

Question: How do children help in your community?

Answer: ______________________________

____

Question: What do you use the kiva for?

Answer: ______________________________

____

Question: I understand you are having a ceremonial dance tomorrow. Where will it be held? What is it for?

Answer: ______________________________

____

Touring Mesa Verde National Park

Use the map of Mesa Verde National Park to complete the questions and activities below. For help, you can look back at pages 88–91 in your book.

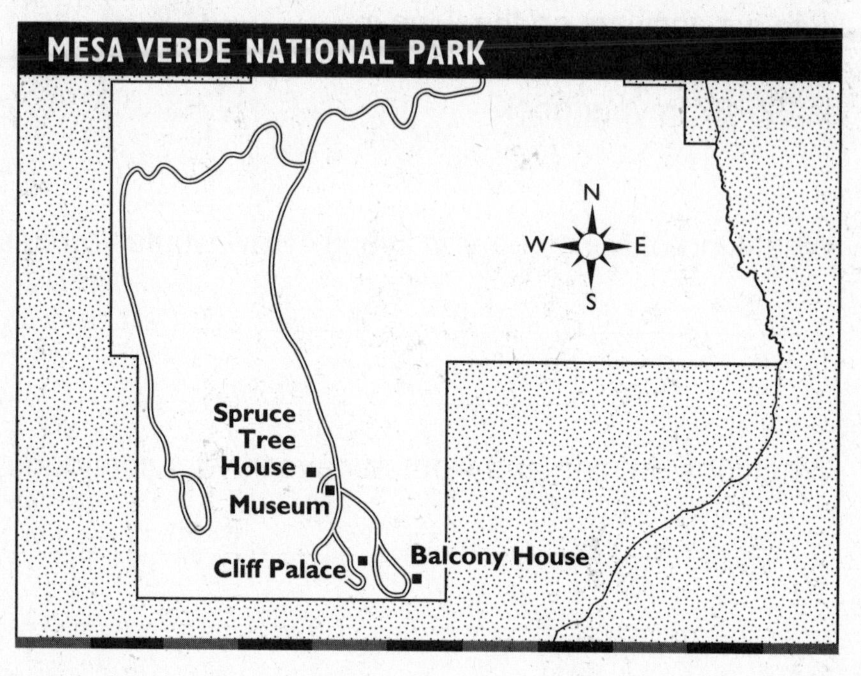

1. Where is the best place to start your tour of Mesa Verde National Park? Circle that place on the map. Why is this a good place to start?

2. What sites would you like to see at Mesa Verde National Park? Draw a line on the map to show your route.

3. What are two important lessons we can learn from the Anasazi?

4. What can we learn by studying the past?

MAKING DECISIONS

Read about the choices Sara must make. Circle the answer to each question. For help, you can look back at pages 92–93 in your book.

1. Sara's goal is to visit the sites in Mesa Verde National Park. It is a warm and sunny day, and she will be hiking from one site to another. She will also have to do some climbing to see the cliff houses. Sara wants to be comfortable and safe. What should she wear?

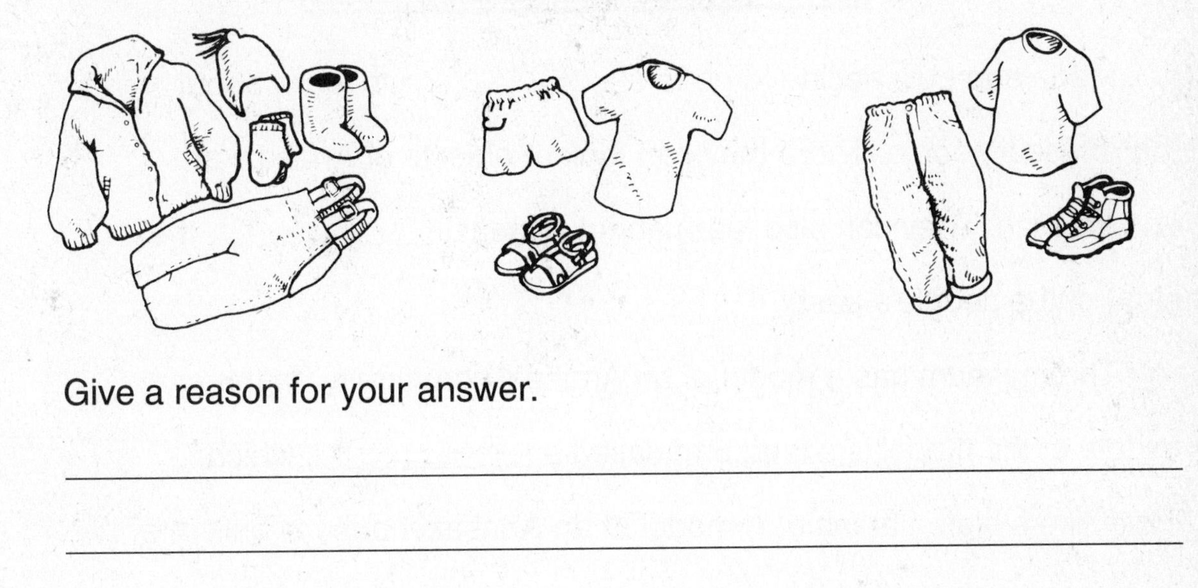

Give a reason for your answer.

____

____

____

2. Sara wants to remember what she sees at Mesa Verde National Park. But she doesn't want to carry too many things. What would be best for her to take along?

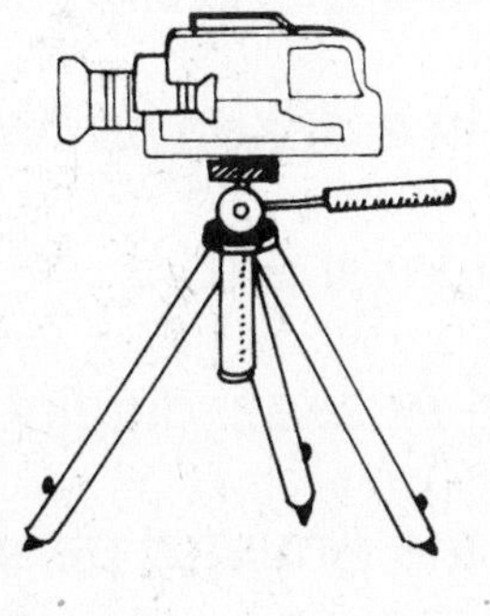

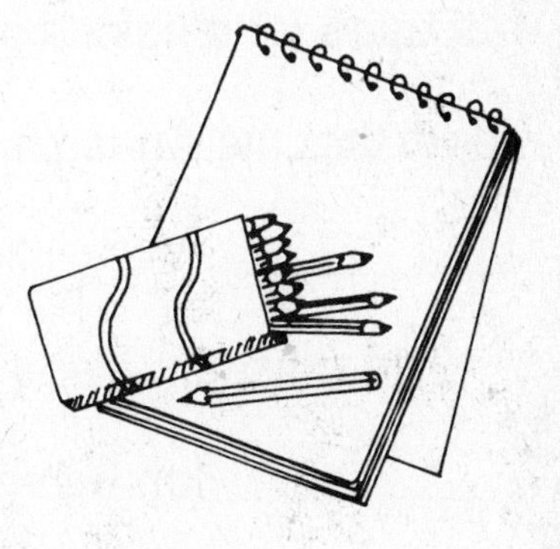

Give a reason for your answer.

____

____

Using New Words

Use the words in the box to complete the sentences below. For help, you can look back at the lessons in Chapter 3 of your book.

history	mesa	technology
desert	cliff	museum
artifact	kiva	canyon

Maria and Luis decide to go to a ____________ to learn about the Anasazi people. There they can look at objects of Anasazi art and science. They can also learn about Anasazi ____________, the story of the people's past.

The museum has a model of an Anasazi community. In the middle of the model is a landform called a ____________, which looks like a high, flat table. A model of an Anasazi house is built into the side of a steep rock face called a ____________. The rock face is part of a deep river valley with steep sides called a ____________. The Anasazi house has a special room called a ____________ that was used for religious purposes. Maria and Luis also learn from the model that the Anasazi lived in a dry environment called a ____________. Very little rain fell there.

The museum also has an Anasazi digging stick. It is an ____________ left behind by the Anasazi people. The digging stick is an example of ____________ because the Anasazi used it to serve their needs.

THE GEOGRAPHY OF JAMESTOWN

Look at the map of Jamestown. Then follow the directions. For help, you can look back at pages 98–101 of your book.

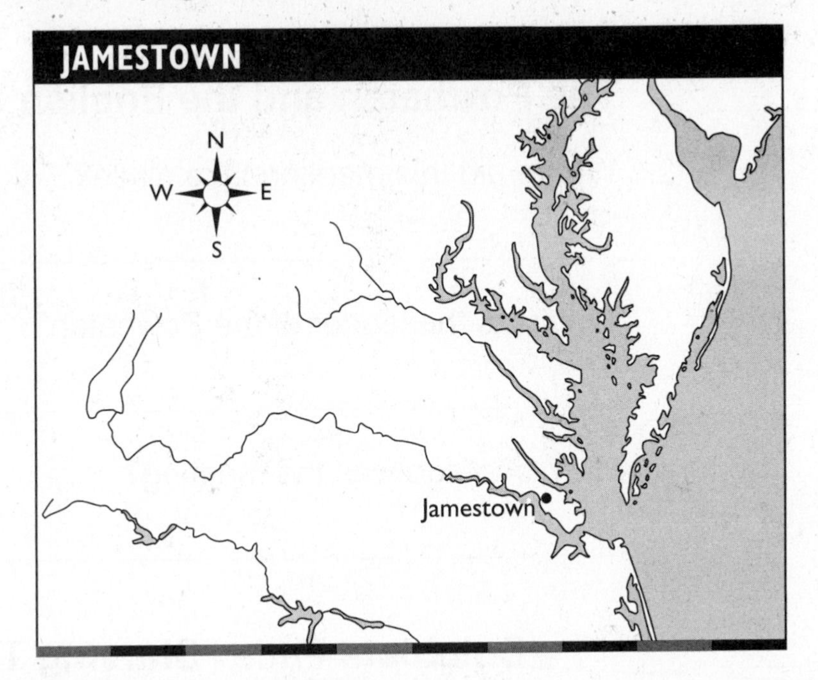

1. Find the part of the map that shows Jamestown. Draw a circle around that part.

   Who was living in this area when the English arrived? ____________

2. Find the James River. Trace it in blue. Then label it.
   What is one way the first people in this area used the river?

   ____

3. Find Chesapeake Bay on the map. Color it blue. Then label it.
   What did Chesapeake Bay provide the English settlers?

   ____

   ____

   What did Chesapeake Bay provide the Powhatan?

   ____

4. Why was the land around Jamestown a good environment for both the Powhatan and the English? ____________

Thinking About Jamestown

Next to each event write the year it took place. Then answer the questions. For help, look back at pages 102–107 in your book.

______________ **The Powhatan and the English First Meet**

Where did this meeting take place?

____

Who was the leader of the Powhatan?

____

How long ago was the meeting?

____

______________ **Colonists Face "Starving Time"**

What happened in Jamestown during this period?

____

____

______________ **Colonists Grow New Kind of Tobacco**

Why was this event important for Jamestown?

____

____

______________ **John Rolfe Marries Pocahontas**

Why was this marriage important?

____

____

WRITING ABOUT JAMESTOWN

Write a guide for people visiting Jamestown Settlement and the Powhatan village. Use the questions and pictures below to help you. Write your answers in complete sentences. For help, you can look back at pages 108–111 in your book.

- Why would people want to visit Jamestown Settlement?
- What would visitors see at the English village?
- What would visitors see docked in the James River?
- What would visitors see in the Powhatan village?

JAMESTOWN'S EARLY HISTORY

Use the time line on this page to answer the questions below. For help, you can look back at pages 112–113 in your book.

1600	1607	1609	1612	1614
Native Americans are living in an area later called Virginia	Colonists arrive at James River to start a new colony	Many colonists die during the "starving time"	John Rolfe grows a new kind of tobacco	Pocahontas marries John Rolfe

1. How many years does the time line cover? ______________________

2. In what year did colonists arrive at the James River? ______________

3. What happened at Jamestown five years after it was founded?

   ____

4. What important event took place in 1614?

   ____

5. How many years ago was the "starving time"?

   ____

Complete the time line below. Show some important events in the recent past. Be sure to include the year you are in now.

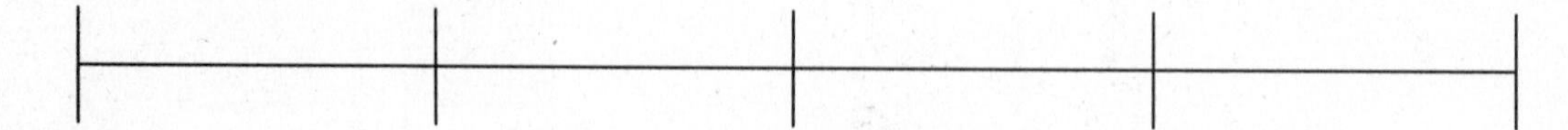

USING NEW WORDS

Use the code to figure out the words. Then write the number of each word next to its meaning. For help, you can look back at the lessons in Chapter 4.

Code

a = z	g = t	l = o	q = j	v = e
b = y	h = s	m = n	r = i	w = d
c = x	i = r	n = m	s = h	x = c
d = w	j = q	o = l	t = g	y = b
e = v	k = p	p = k	u = f	z = a
f = u				

1. xlolmb

____

2. orermt srhglib nfhvfn

____

3. yzb

____

4. hozevib

____

5. xlolmrhg

____

6. xlzhgzo kozrm

____

_____ **a.** a body of water partly surrounded by land

_____ **b.** flat land along a coast

_____ **c.** a place that is ruled by another country

_____ **d.** someone who lives in a colony

_____ **e.** the practice of one person owning another

_____ **f.** a place where people dress, talk, and do things as they did long ago

Name: Use with pages 118–121.

THINKING ABOUT SAN ANTONIO

Use the map of San Antonio to help you complete the following activities. For help, you can refer to pages 118–121 of your book.

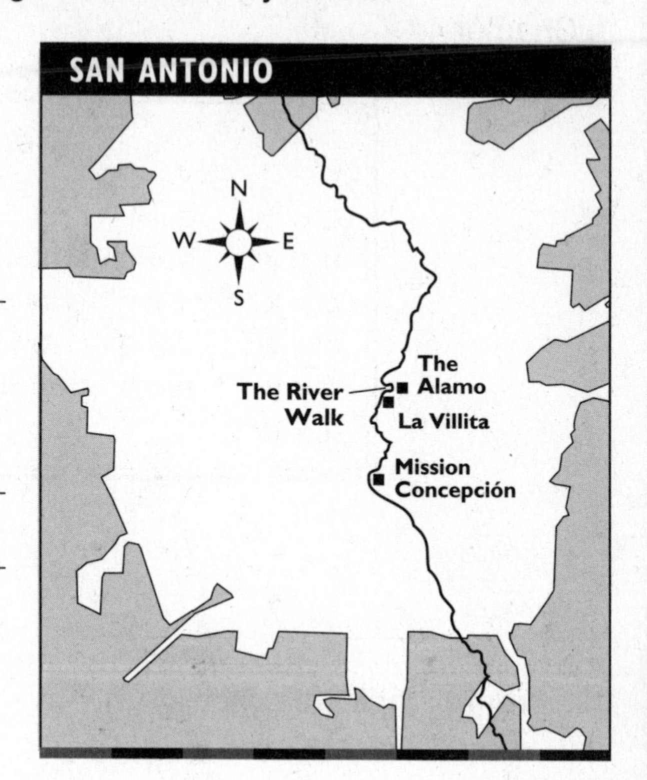

1. Find the San Antonio River. Trace it in blue. Then label it.

2. Which Native American group lived along this river?

   ____

   What did their name for the river mean in English?

   ____

   ____

3. What did the people of San Antonio build along the river in the 1920s?

   ____

   What was the original hope for it? ______________________________

   ____

4. Until the 1950s what was much of the land around the river used for?

   ____

   Why was the land especially good for what it was used for?

   ____

   ____

5. How is the river important to the people of San Antonio today?

   ____

   ____

WRITING ABOUT THE SPANISH MISSIONS

Use the space provided to answer the questions in each box. Write your answers in complete sentences. For help, look back at pages 122–127 in your book.

- What were the missions?
- Who set them up?
- Why were they set up?

- What did the missions offer Native Americans?
- What did Native Americans have to do in return?

- How did the way of life of many Native Americans change because of the missions?

SAN ANTONIO CELEBRATES ITS PAST

Draw a line from the first question in each group to the picture that answers it. Write the answers to the other question. For help, you can look back at pages 128–132 in your book.

1. Which picture shows one of San Antonio's old missions?

How are the missions used today?

____

____

2. Which picture shows San Antonio's biggest celebration?

What is this celebration called?

____

What special day does it include?

____

What does that day celebrate?

____

____

3. Which picture shows a popular game played in San Antonio?

Where did this game come from?

____

Name: Use with pages 134–135.

USING GRAPHS

Study the graphs below. Then answer each question. For help, you can look back at pages 134–135 in your book.

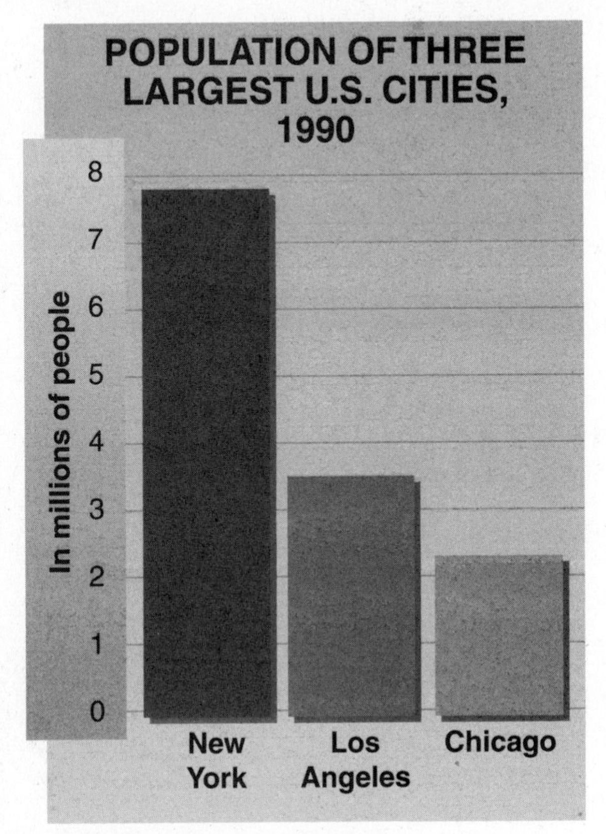

Source: *The World Almanac and Book of Facts, 1995*

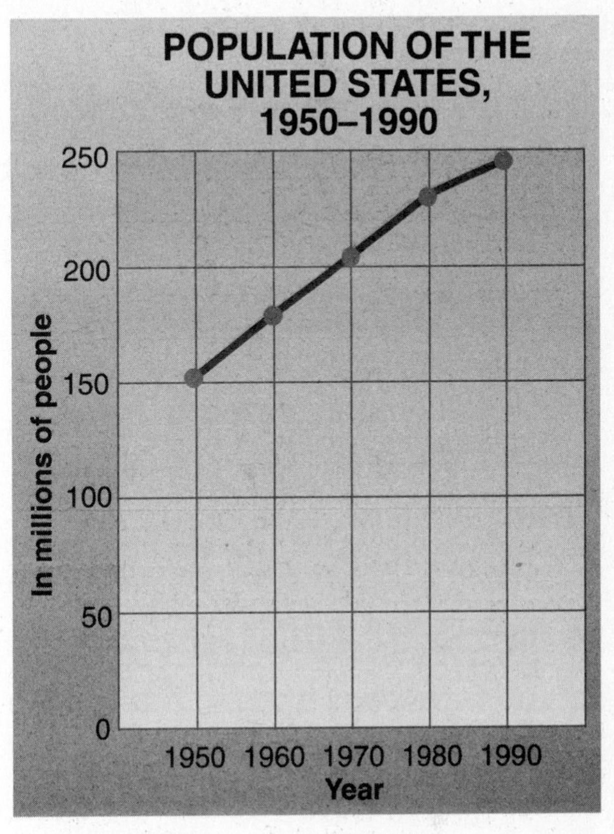

Source: *The World Almanac and Book of Facts, 1995*

1. What are graphs such as the one above used for?

____

____

2. About how many people lived in New York City in 1990?

____

3. Which city on the graph had the smallest population in 1990?

____

4. What are graphs such as the one above used for?

____

____

5. What was the population of the United States in 1990?

____

6. How did the population of the United States change from 1950 to 1990?

____

FINDING AND USING NEW WORDS

Follow the directions to find each hidden word. Then write the word.

1. Cross out the letters *c, p,* and *b.*
   p c f b i c e b c s p b b t p c c a ____________

2. Cross out the letters *b, w,* and *u.*
   w m b i b u b s s w u i b o b n w b a w u r y ____________

3. Cross out the letters *z, r,* and *g.*
   c r g a z z c g r t z r g u g r s ____________

4. Cross out the letters *k, s,* and *m.*
   i k s n m d s k e p s m e n k d m e n s c s e m ____________

5. Cross out the letters *y, d,* and *x.*
   d y m x i y d s y s d x i d o x n ____________

6. Cross out the letters *w, h,* and *m.*
   w h v o m w l h u n m h t e m w e r h ____________

Write each hidden word next to its meaning. For help, you can look back at the lessons in Chapter 5 of your book.

7. a priest who sets up a mission ____________
8. a Spanish word that means "festival" ____________
9. a type of plant with sharp spines that grows in a dry environment ____________
10. freedom from others ____________
11. a community set up by Roman Catholic priests to teach their religion to others ____________
12. someone who does something by choice and without pay ____________

Writing About Benjamin Franklin

Use the space provided to answer the questions in each box. Write your answers as sentences in a paragraph. Your paragraphs will be a summary of important facts about Benjamin Franklin. For help, you can look back at pages 146–151 in your textbook.

Benjamin Franklin

- Where did Benjamin Franklin grow up?
- Where did he move when he was 17?
- Why was this an important place?
- What popular book did Benjamin Franklin begin writing a few years after he moved?
- What are two ways Benjamin Franklin helped his community?

- How did Benjamin Franklin help America in 1776?
- What statement did he and other leaders adopt on July 4, 1776?
- Why was this statement important?

OUR PLAN OF GOVERNMENT

Use the pictures on the right to complete the activities on this page. For help, you can look back at pages 154–159 in your textbook.

1. a. Draw a line to the picture that shows where our plan of government is described.

b. What are the three branches of government named in the plan?

____

____

____

2. a. Draw a line to the picture of the person who suggested three branches of government.

b. How did this person help us know what happened at the meeting in which the Constitution was written?

____

____

3. a. Draw a line to the picture of the person who became our country's first President.

b. How is the President chosen?

____

c. What is the President's job?

____

____

George Washington

United States Constitution

James Madison

COMPARING AND CONTRASTING

Think about how Benjamin Franklin and George Washington were alike and different. Underline the answer to each question. For help, you can look back at pages 160–161 in your textbook.

Benjamin Franklin

George Washington

1. Where was Benjamin Franklin's home?
   a. Philadelphia
   b. Virginia
   c. New York

2. What did Franklin want the colonies to become?
   a. part of England
   b. an independent country
   c. a state

3. What did Benjamin Franklin do in 1776?
   a. led America's whole army
   b. took part in adopting the Declaration of Independence
   c. wrote the Declaration of Independence

4. What did Franklin do in 1787?
   a. stayed home
   b. helped write the Constitution
   c. took notes at the convention

5. Where was George Washington's home?
   a. Philadelphia
   b. Virginia
   c. New York

6. What did Washington want the colonies to become?
   a. part of England
   b. an independent country
   c. a state

7. What did George Washington do in 1776?
   a. led America's whole army
   b. took part in adopting the Declaration of Independence
   c. wrote the Declaration of Independence

8. What did Washington do in 1787?
   a. stayed home
   b. helped write the Constitution
   c. took notes at the convention

USING NEW WORDS

Finish each sentence by matching a word or term in the box with its meaning. For help, look at the lessons in Chapter 6 of your textbook.

tax	American Revolution	Bill of Rights
elect	Declaration of Independence	Constitution
almanac	Supreme Court	compromise
Congress	President	

1. A book that comes out every year is an ________________.
2. Money that people pay to support the government is a ________.
3. The fighting that began in 1775 between the colonists and the English is called the ________________________.
4. The statement about why the colonies should be free is called the ____________________________.
5. The laws and plan for how the government of our country works is called the ________________.
6. To choose by voting is to ________________.
7. The settlement of an argument by each side agreeing to give up some of its demands is a ________________.
8. The part of the government made up of the Senate and the House of Representatives is the ________________.
9. The leader of our country is the ________________.
10. The part of government that makes sure our laws are fair is the ________________.
11. The list of our country's most important rights and freedoms is the ________________.

DECIDING ON OUR NATION'S CAPITAL

Answer the following questions by using the map and pages 166–169 in your book.

1. What does the map show?

____

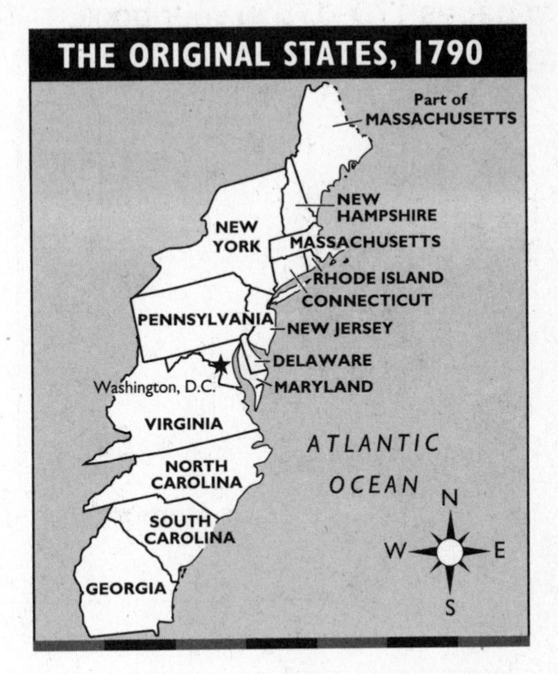

2. Look closely at the map. Circle the name of the city that is the capital of our country.

3. Why did the leaders of the United States have trouble deciding where to build the capital city?

____

____

____

____

____

4. How is the location of our country's capital a compromise?

____

5. What do you think it was like to live in the capital during the time of John Adams?

____

____

____

Name:

A Visit to Washington, D.C.

Look at these pictures of memorials in Washington, D.C. Write a fact about each one in the space below. For help, you can look back at pages 170–175 in your book.

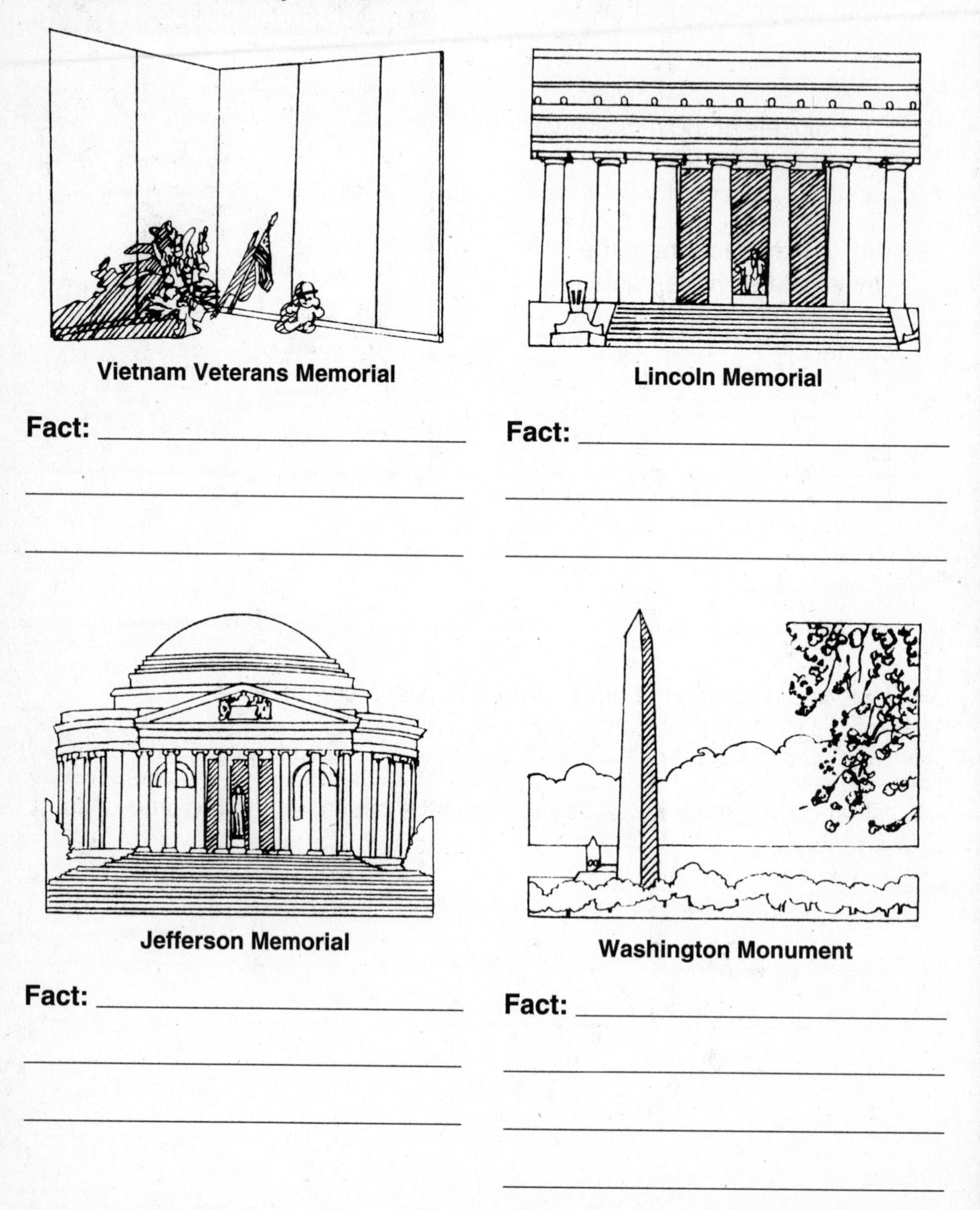

Vietnam Veterans Memorial

Fact: ______________________

____

____

Lincoln Memorial

Fact: ______________________

____

____

Jefferson Memorial

Fact: ______________________

____

____

Washington Monument

Fact: ______________________

____

____

____

FINDING PLACES ON A GRID MAP

Complete the index for this grid map of Washington, D.C. Write each place name in the index box. Next to the name write the place's location on the map. The first one has been done for you. For help, you can look back at pages 176–177 in your textbook.

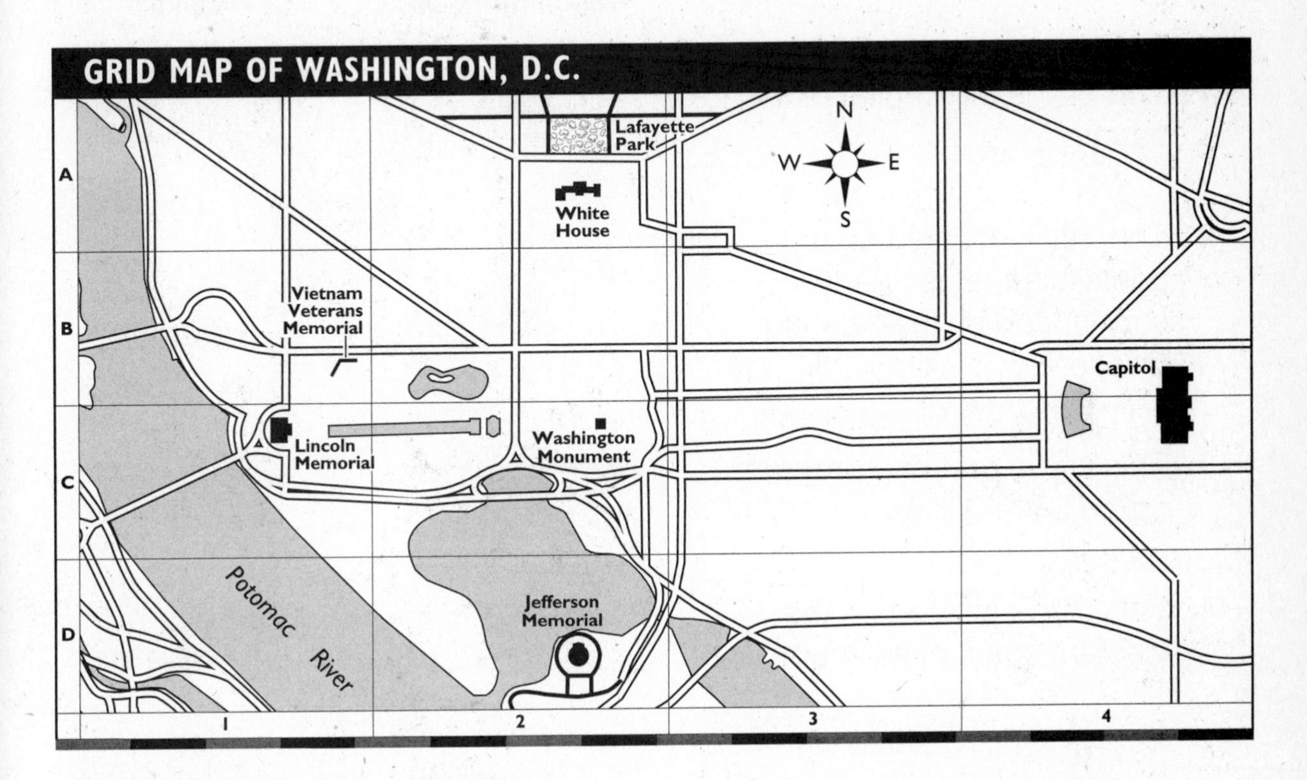

INDEX

PLACE	LOCATION ON MAP
Capitol	B4–C4

Comparing Capitals

Read each clue. Then circle the picture of the city each clue tells about. If a clue tells about both cities, circle both pictures. For help, you can look back at pages 178–181 in your textbook.

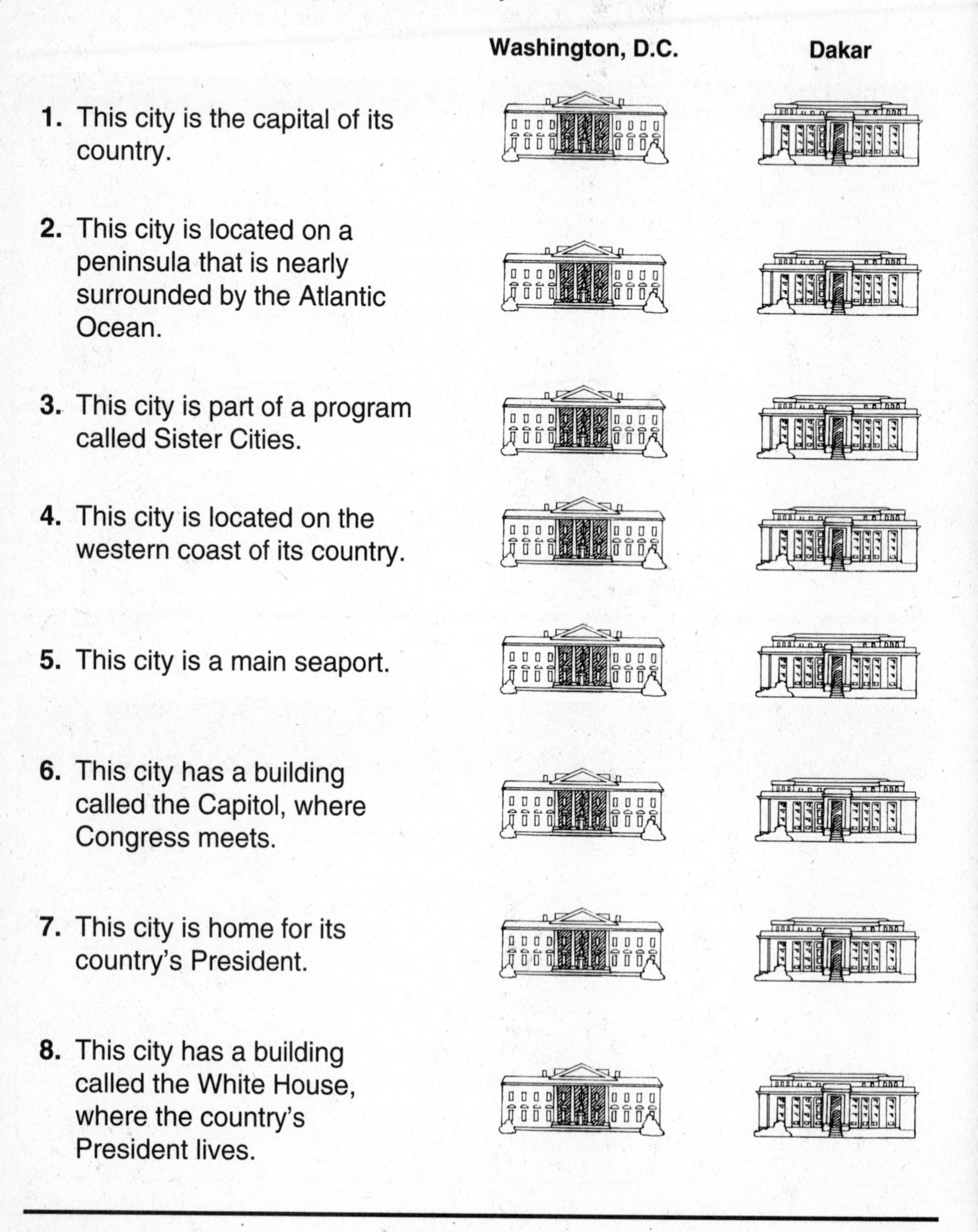

Washington, D.C. **Dakar**

1. This city is the capital of its country.
2. This city is located on a peninsula that is nearly surrounded by the Atlantic Ocean.
3. This city is part of a program called Sister Cities.
4. This city is located on the western coast of its country.
5. This city is a main seaport.
6. This city has a building called the Capitol, where Congress meets.
7. This city is home for its country's President.
8. This city has a building called the White House, where the country's President lives.

Thinking About New Words

Put an **X** next to each statement that correctly uses the word in dark print. For help, you can look back at the lessons in Chapter 7 of your textbook.

1. ambassador

_____ **a.** An ambassador is a person who is the head of a city government.

_____ **b.** An ambassador is a person who is sent to another country to represent his or her country.

_____ **c.** An ambassador goes to another country to join the parliament of that country.

2. capital

_____ **a.** A capital is the place where the government of a country or state is located.

_____ **b.** Washington, D.C., is the capital of the United States.

_____ **c.** A capital is a reminder of a person or event.

3. mayor

_____ **a.** A mayor is the head of a city government.

_____ **b.** A mayor is the leader of a country.

_____ **c.** George Washington was the mayor of Washington, D.C.

4. memorial

_____ **a.** A memorial is a reminder of a person or event.

_____ **b.** A memorial is the place where the government of a country or state is located.

_____ **c.** The Jefferson Memorial is located in Washington, D.C.

State and Local Government

Look at the pictures and read the questions. Draw a line under each correct answer. For help, look back at pages 186–189 in your textbook.

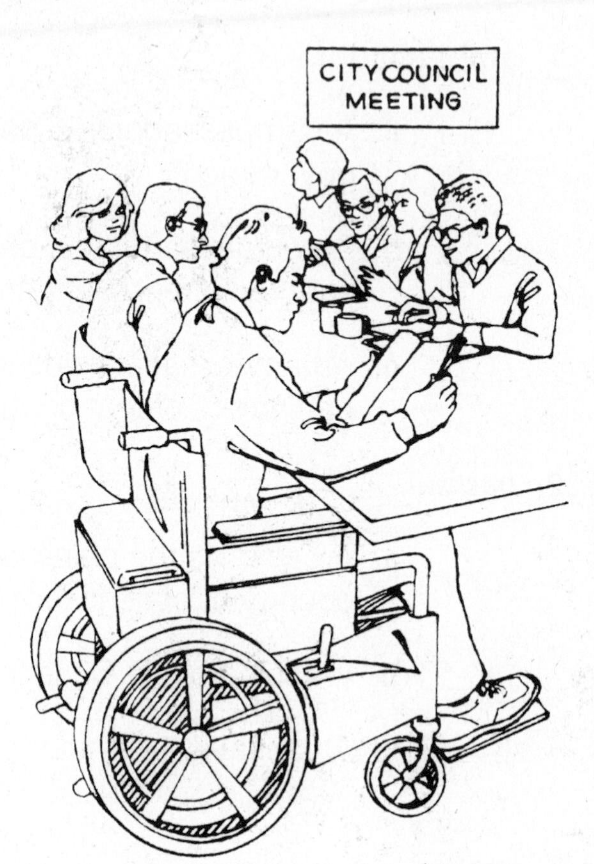

1. What group of people is having a meeting?
   a. members of a city council
   b. members of a town meeting
2. Which kind of government is the group a part of?
   a. local government
   b. state government
3. How is this group chosen?
   a. may be chosen by the mayor
   b. may be elected
4. What job does this group have?
   a. makes sure laws are obeyed
   b. makes laws for the city

5. Who is this person?
   a. a mayor
   b. a governor
6. What kind of government is this person a part of?
   a. local government
   b. state government
7. What does the governor do?
   a. helps make state laws
   b. chooses mayors for the cities

USING A LIBRARY

The students of Shapleigh, Maine, want to make a guide to the wildlife they see in their park. Follow the directions to show how they can complete their guide. For help, you can look back at pages 190–191 in your textbook.

1. The students want to include the birds they see in their park. Circle the sign in the picture that tells where they would find this information.

2. The students want to include a book called *A Field Guide to the Birds* by Roger Tory Peterson. Where in the nonfiction section would they look? Circle your answer.

in the animal section in the gardening section

3. The students want to include information about robins. Which book would help them? Circle your answer.

dictionary encyclopedia

Put an **X** on the sign in the picture that names the section where they would find this book.

4. Suppose the students looked up the word *robin* in the encyclopedia. The guide words at the top of the page they turned to were *river* and *rope*. Circle the words that tell where they would find the topic they wanted.

before this page on this page after this page

5. Some students want to include made-up stories about animals. Draw a line under the sign in the picture that names the section where they would find these stories.

BEING A GOOD CITIZEN

On the lines, list three ways that you can be a good citizen in your community. Then circle one of the ways. Make a poster in the space below that shows you being a good citizen in the way you circled. For help, you can look back at pages 192–197 in your textbook.

Using New Words

Use the code to figure out the words. Then write the number of each word next to its meaning. For help, you can look back at the lessons in Chapter 8 of your textbook.

Code

a = b	g = n	l = x	q = s	v = i
b = d	h = p	m = z	r = q	w = g
c = f	i = r	n = y	s = o	x = e
d = h	j = t	o = w	t = m	y = c
e = j	k = v	p = u	u = k	z = a
f = l				

1. f s y z f w s k x i g t x g j

____

2. H f x b w x s c Z f f x w v z g y x

____

3. w s k x i g s i

____

4. j s o g t x x j v g w

____

5. y v j n y s p g y v f

____

_____ **a.** the head of each state's government

_____ **b.** the government in each city or community

_____ **c.** a group of elected people who make the laws for a city

_____ **d.** a type of local government in which people come together to decide on the laws and rules that are important to their community

_____ **e.** words people say promising to be loyal to our country

TRAVELING WEST

Use the map below to complete the activities on this page. For help, you can look back at pages 210–215 in your textbook.

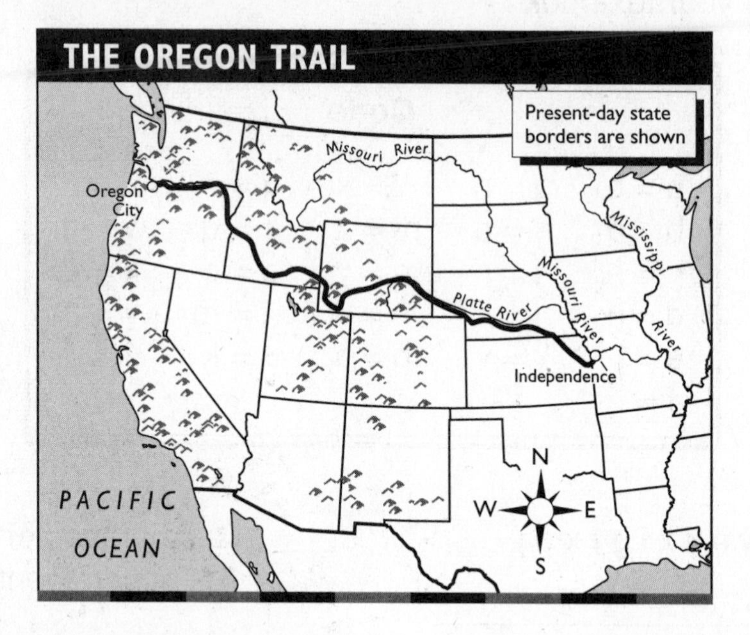

1. The map shows one of the trails that many pioneers took west. What is the name of this trail?

____

2. Circle the city on the map where the trail began. Why was this a good place to begin the trail?

____

____

____

3. According to the map, which large mountain range did the pioneers have to cross?

____

Label this range on the map.

4. How did groups of pioneers travel along this trail?

____

What were some of the hardships they encountered?

____

____

____

____

____

5. Why did so many pioneers make this dangerous journey?

____

____

Planning a Camping Trip

Larry and his family are planning a camping trip. Look at the pictures of the things Larry would like to take. Then use the lines below to classify the things that Larry really needs to take and what he doesn't really need to take. For help, you can look back at pages 216–217 in your textbook.

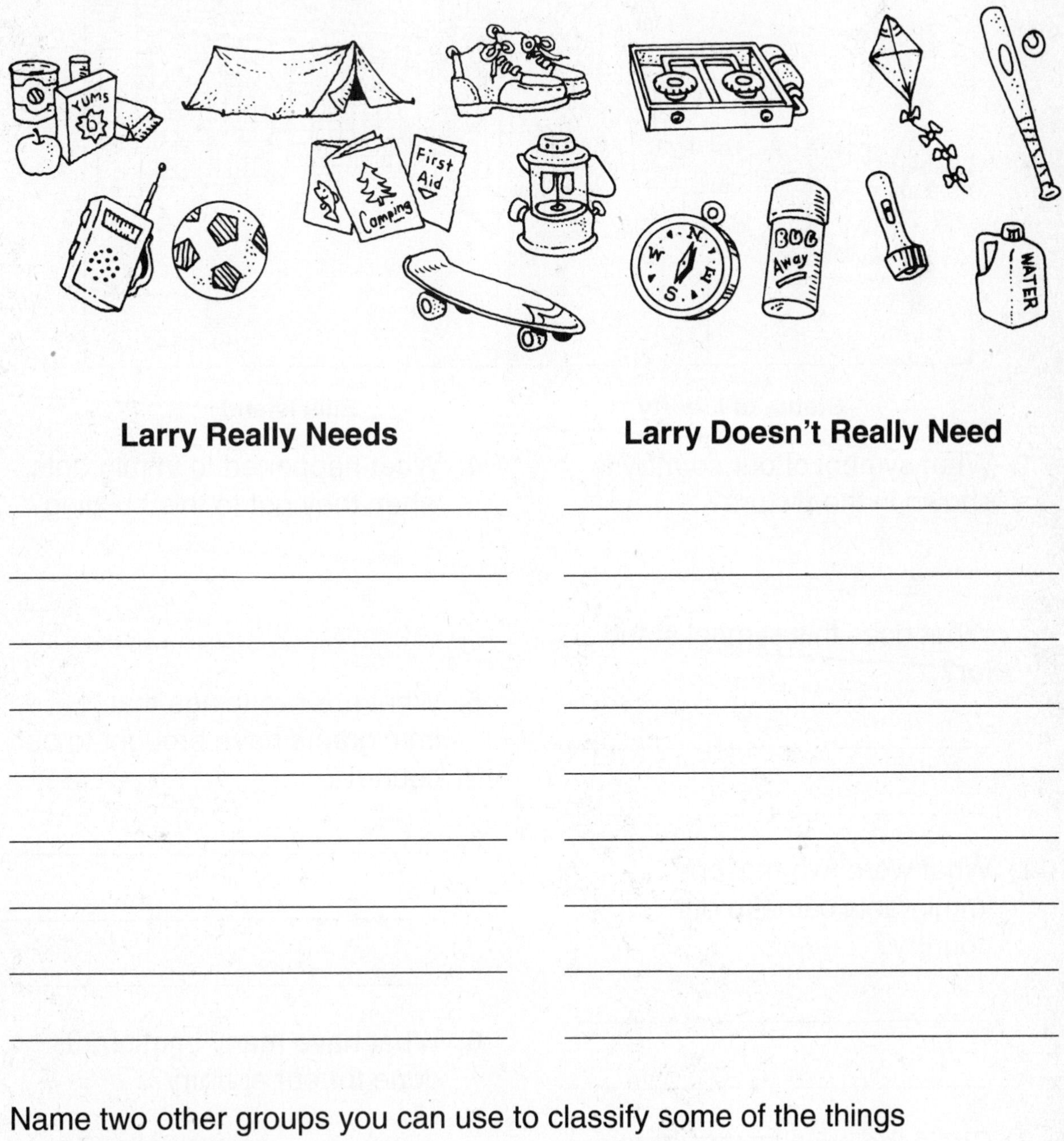

Larry Really Needs

Larry Doesn't Really Need

Name two other groups you can use to classify some of the things Larry wants to take.

Name:

Immigrants in the Early 1900s

Use the pictures below to complete the activities on this page. For help, you can look back at pages 218–223 in your textbook.

Statue of Liberty

Ellis Island

1. What symbol of our country is shown in the picture?

____

What does this symbol stand for?

____

____

2. What were two reasons immigrants came to our country?

____

____

3. Circle the building that shows where many immigrants were taken.

4. What happened to immigrants when they got to this building?

____

____

5. What are two things that immigrants have brought to our country?

____

____

____

6. What have many immigrants done for our country?

____

____

ON THE ROAD TO FREEDOM

Use the pictures on the right to complete the activities on this page. For help, you can look back at pages 224–229 in your textbook.

1. **a.** Draw a line to the picture of the man who was President during the Civil War.

   b. Who fought against each other in this war?

   ____

   ____

   c. What did this President want to do during the Civil War?

   ____

2. **a.** Draw a line to the picture of a painter.

   b. What event were his paintings about?

   ____

   c. Why did this event take place?

   ____

   ____

3. **a.** Draw a line to the picture of a famous leader in the 1950s and 1960s.

   b. What did this man spend his life doing?

   ____

   ____

Martin Luther King, Jr.

Abraham Lincoln

Jacob Lawrence

Talking with Delores Stivalet

Suppose you had a chance to interview Delores Stivalet, the girl described in Lesson 4. You might ask her questions similar to the ones below. Write Delores's answers in the space provided. For help, you can look back at pages 232–236 in your textbook.

Question: You and your family are immigrants to the United States. What country and city are you from?

Delores: ____________________

Question: Why did your family decide to move to the United States?

Delores: ____________________

____

Question: You are now living in San Diego. How is San Diego like Veracruz?

Delores: ____________________

____

Question: What is the main difference between the two cities?

Delores: ____________________

____

____

Question: What do you miss about your old home?

Delores: ____________________

____

Question: What do you hope will happen someday?

Delores: ____________________

____

Using New Words

Write the word or term from the box below that best matches each description. For help, you can look back at the lessons in Chapter 9 of your textbook.

oath	pioneer	oral history
diary	migration	immigrant
prairie	Civil War	Great Migration

1. flat or rolling land covered with tall grasses ______________________

2. a person who is among the first to explore and settle an area that is not known to him or her ______________________

3. a written record of what someone has done or thought each day ______________________

4. someone who comes to live in a new country ______________________

5. telling stories about what life was like in the past ______________________

6. the movement of people from one part of a country or area to another ______________________

7. the movement north by thousands of African Americans beginning around 1915 ______________________

8. the war in which the Northern and Southern parts of the United States fought each other ______________________

9. a statement or promise in which a person swears that what he or she says is true ______________________

IMPROVEMENTS IN TRANSPORTATION

Look at each picture. Name the improvement in transportation it shows. Then answer the questions. For help, you can look back at pages 242–247 in your textbook.

Improvement: ____________________

____

Who built it? ____________________

How did it improve transportation?

____

____

____

____

Improvement: ____________________

____

Who built it? ____________________

How did it improve transportation?

____

____

____

____

Name two other important improvements in transportation.

____________________ ____________________

On the lines that follow, explain how these improvements have helped bring people closer together.

____

____

____

Reading a Transportation Map

Use the map to complete the activities. For help, you can look back at pages 248–249 in your textbook.

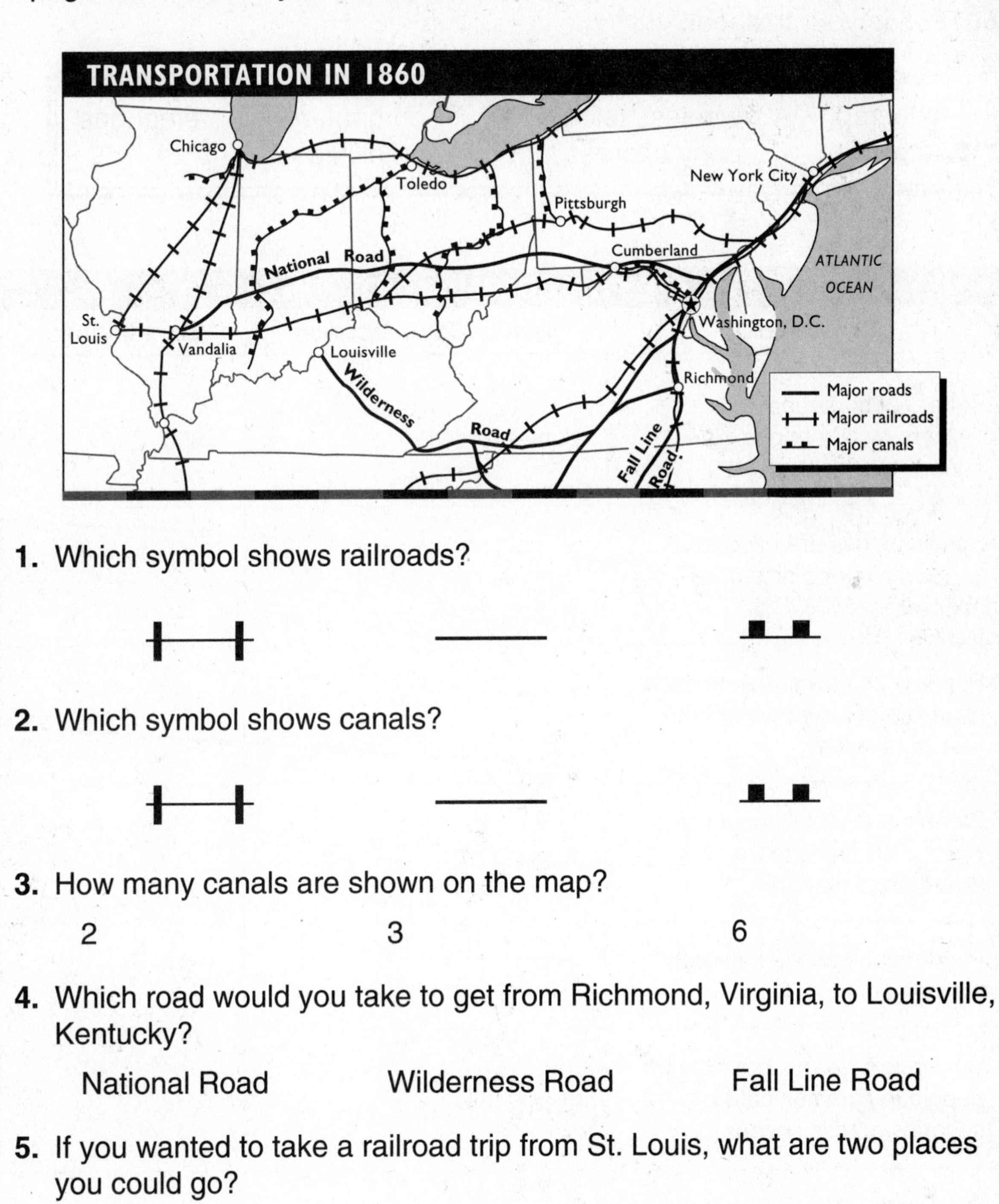

1. Which symbol shows railroads?

2. Which symbol shows canals?

3. How many canals are shown on the map?

   2   3   6

4. Which road would you take to get from Richmond, Virginia, to Louisville, Kentucky?

   National Road   Wilderness Road   Fall Line Road

5. If you wanted to take a railroad trip from St. Louis, what are two places you could go?

____

____

Thinking About Communication

Use the terms from the box to complete the chart below. Some information has been filled in for you. For help, look at pages 250–255 in your textbook.

telegraph	wireless telegraph	computers	telephone
television	pony express	satellites	

TYPES OF COMMUNICATION

Description	Kind of Communication	Date Invented
A team of horseback riders delivers mail from one place to another across the West.	pony express	1860
Special codes are used to send words long distances over wires.		
People can now speak to each other directly over wires from faraway places.		
Signals are sent without using wires. This leads to the invention of the radio.		
Pictures and sounds are sent through space.		1936
Spacecraft make it possible for people to communicate in seconds across oceans.		1962
People send and receive written information and pictures every day.		1990s

Two Countries and a Tunnel

Look at the picture. Then answer the questions. For help, you can look back at pages 256–261 in your textbook.

1. What event does the boy's newspaper tell about? ____________________

____

2. In which year did this event take place? ____________________

3. Which two countries took part in this event? ____________________

____

4. What did this event do for the first time? ____________________

____

5. Why was this tunnel built? ____________________

____

6. How did this tunnel bring the people in these two countries closer together?

____

____

____

____

Learning New Words

Use the Morse code to figure out each word below. Then write the word on the long line. For help, look at the lessons in Chapter 10 of your textbook.

Morse Code

a = •—	g = ——•	l = •—••	q = ——•—	v = •••—
b = —•••	h = ••••	m = ——	r = •—•	w = •——
c = —•—•	i = ••	n = —•	s = •••	x = —••—
d = —••	j = •———	o = ———	t = —	y = —•——
e = •	k = —•—	p = •——•	u = ••—	z = ——••
f = ••—•				

1. — • •—•• • ——• •—• •— •——• •••• ______________

2. —•—• ——— —— —— ••— —• •• —•—• •— — • ______________

3. ••—• ••— • •—•• ______________

4. •——• ——— —• —•—— • —••— •——• •—• • ••• ••• ______________ ______________

5. —•—• •••• •— —• —• • •—•• ______________

6. ••• •— — • •—•• •—•• •• — • ______________

Write the number of each word from the list above next to its meaning.

_____ **a.** something that is burned to produce power

_____ **b.** a narrow waterway between two larger bodies of water

_____ **c.** a machine that used special codes to send words long distances over wires

_____ **d.** a spacecraft that connects radio, telephone, and television communication

_____ **e.** to pass along feelings, thoughts, or information to each other

_____ **f.** a team of horseback riders who rode across the western United States to deliver mail from one place to another

THINKING ABOUT JOBS AND MONEY

The picture shows Mr. Bowan's kite store in a small town. Put an **X** next to each sentence that tells something true about Mr. Bowan and his store. Then answer the question. For help, you can look back at pages 274–278 in your textbook.

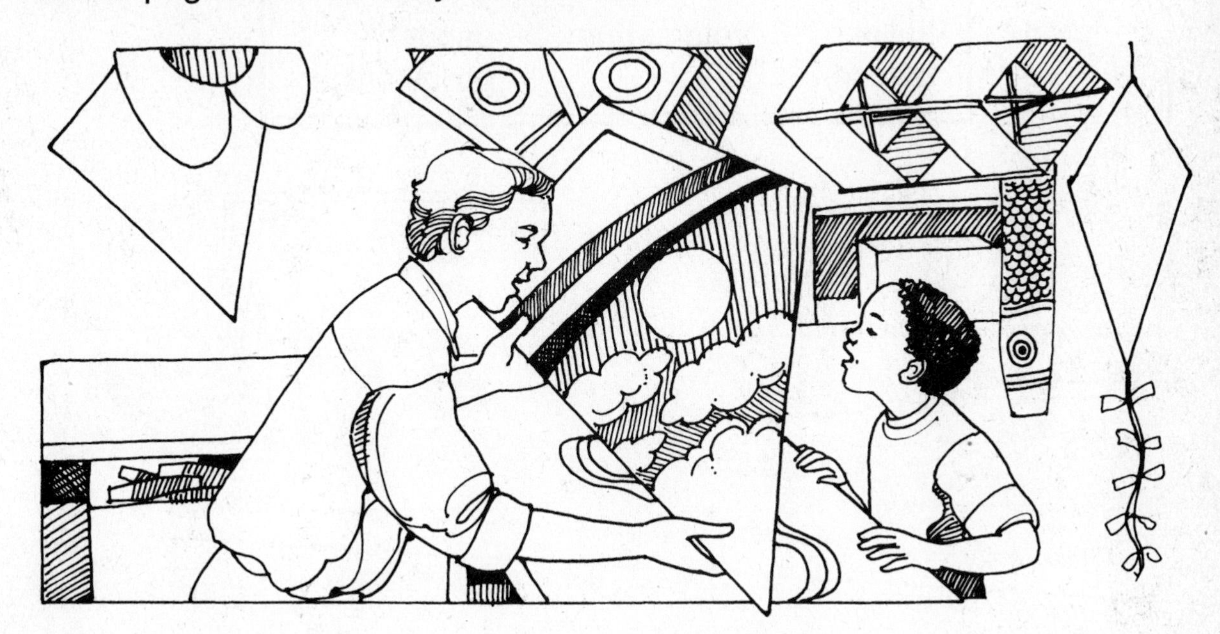

_____ **1.** Mr. Bowan makes a living by selling kites.

_____ **2.** The kites sold in the store are goods.

_____ **3.** The person buying a kite is a consumer.

_____ **4.** Mr. Bowan offers a service by selling and putting together kites.

_____ **5.** The people who work for Mr. Bowan are his employers.

_____ **6.** Mr. Bowan's store is part of the economy of his town.

You are a consumer. Name two kinds of goods that you buy.

____

WHAT KIND OF JOB?

Each picture shows a person doing a job. Label each picture with a job from the box. Then answer the question at the bottom of the page. For help, you can look back at pages 280–287 in your textbook.

builder	veterinarian	dancer
teacher		police officer

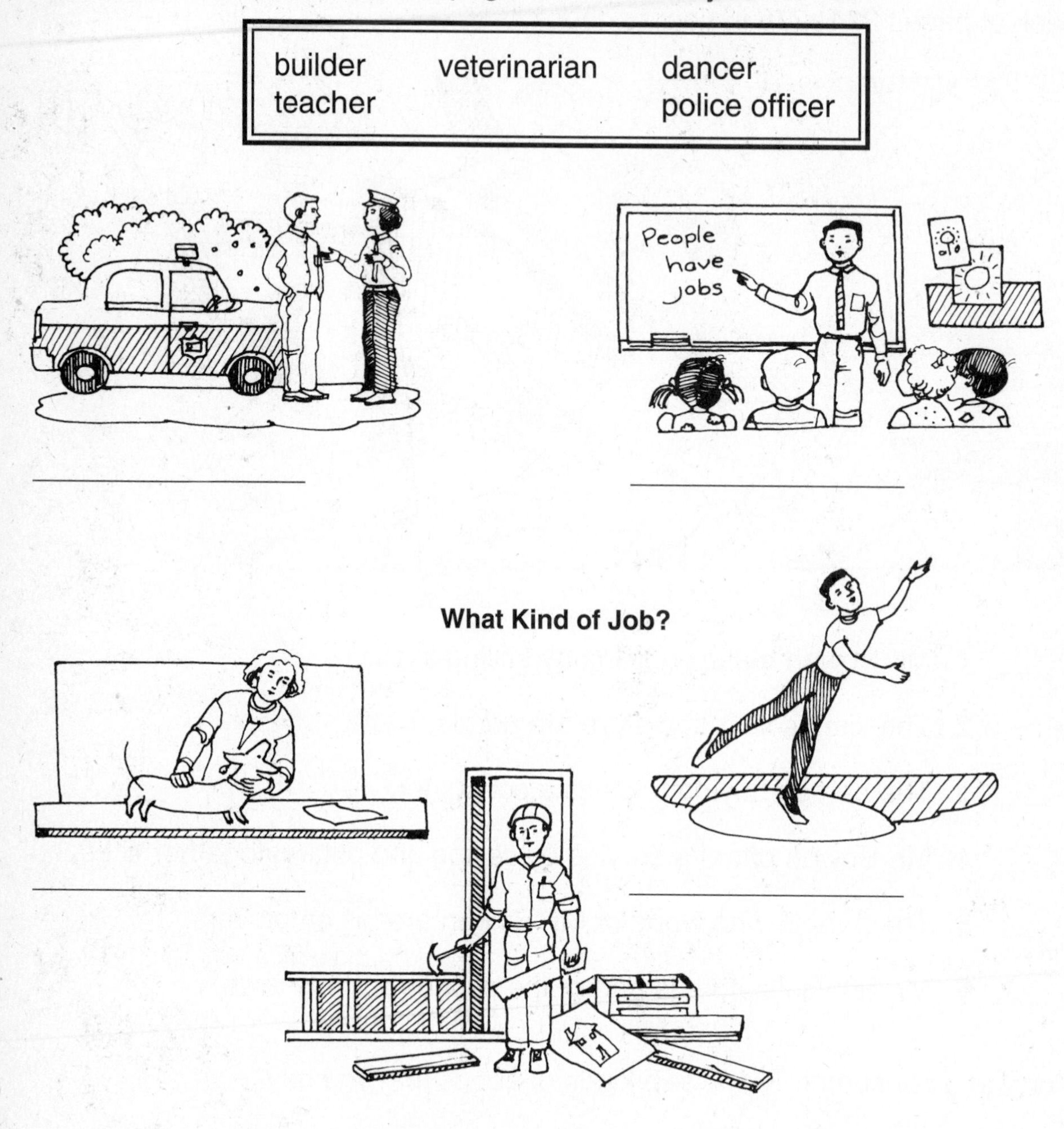

What are some of the jobs of people you know in your community?

Thinking About Cause and Effect

Read the sentences below. Draw a circle around the sentence or sentence part that states the cause. Underline the sentence or sentence part that states the effect. For help, you can look back at pages 290–291 in your textbook.

1. Ms. Kim works hard to make textbooks interesting. As a result, children like to read and learn from her books.

2. Ms. Kim's textbooks are interesting to read because she does research to find interesting topics for the books she plans.

3. Since it takes many steps to make a textbook, many people are needed to work on it.

4. Authors and editors use computers to make changes in the books they are working on. As a result, they can make many more changes in a small amount of time.

5. Designers choose pictures and designs that children will like so the book is exciting and fun to look at.

How can understanding cause and effect connections be helpful?

____

____

____

A VISIT TO JAPAN

Use the pictures on the right to complete the activities on this page. For help, you can look back at pages 292–295 in your textbook.

1. a. Draw a line to the picture that shows the country called "the land of the rising sun."

   b. What is the real name for this country?

   ____

   c. What is this country's capital?

   ____

2. a. Draw a line to the picture that shows a high-tech product made in Japan.

   b. List two other high-tech products made here.

   ____

   ____

3. a. Draw a line to the picture that shows an example of Japan's culture.

   b. What is this event called?

   ____

   c. List two more examples of Japanese culture that were pictured in your textbook.

   ____

   ____

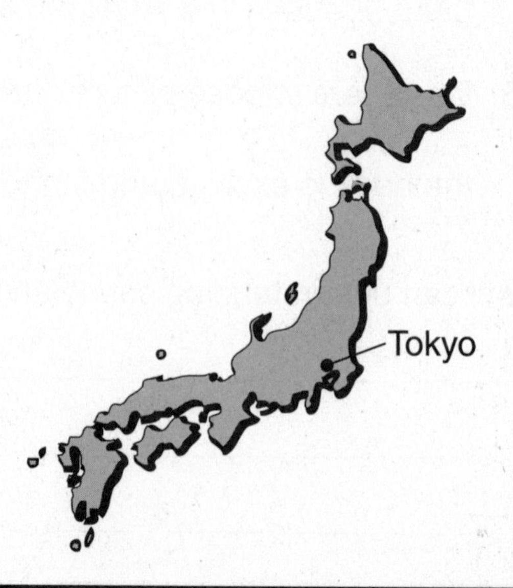

Using New Words

Match each word in the box to its meaning. For help, you can look back at the lessons in Chapter 11 of your textbook.

editor	services	designer	consumer
goods	economy	journalist	publishing
interest	employer	producer	high-tech

1. a person who writes for a newspaper, magazine, or television news program

____

2. jobs that help other people by providing things they need or want

____

3. someone who hires and pays other people to work

____

4. payment for lending money

____

5. a person who buys goods and services

____

6. the making and consuming of goods and services

____

7. things that people make or grow

____

8. a person who makes sure each page of a book looks good

____

9. a maker of goods and services

____

10. making books, magazines, CD-ROMs, and other things people can read

____

11. a person who helps with all the steps involved in making a book

____

12. the use of the latest technology to make electronics and other goods

____

ON THE FARM

Suppose you could interview Jon Lofgreen. You might ask him questions like the ones below. Write Mr. Lofgreen's answers in the space provided. For help, look back at pages 300–305 in your textbook.

Question: What farm products do you produce?

Mr. Lofgreen: ______________________

____

Question: What is most of your farmland used for?

Mr. Lofgreen: ______________________

Question: When do you plant your wheat crop and when do you harvest it?

Mr. Lofgreen: ______________________

____

Question: What happens to the wheat in the winter and spring?

Mr. Lofgreen: ______________________

____

____

Question: What happens to the wheat after it is harvested?

Mr. Lofgreen: ______________________

____

____

Question: How do you depend on technology to run your farm?

Mr. Lofgreen: ______________________

____

____

READING A FLOW CHART

A flow chart shows a sequence of steps. Study the flow chart on this page. Then answer the questions. For help, you can look back at pages 306–307 in your textbook.

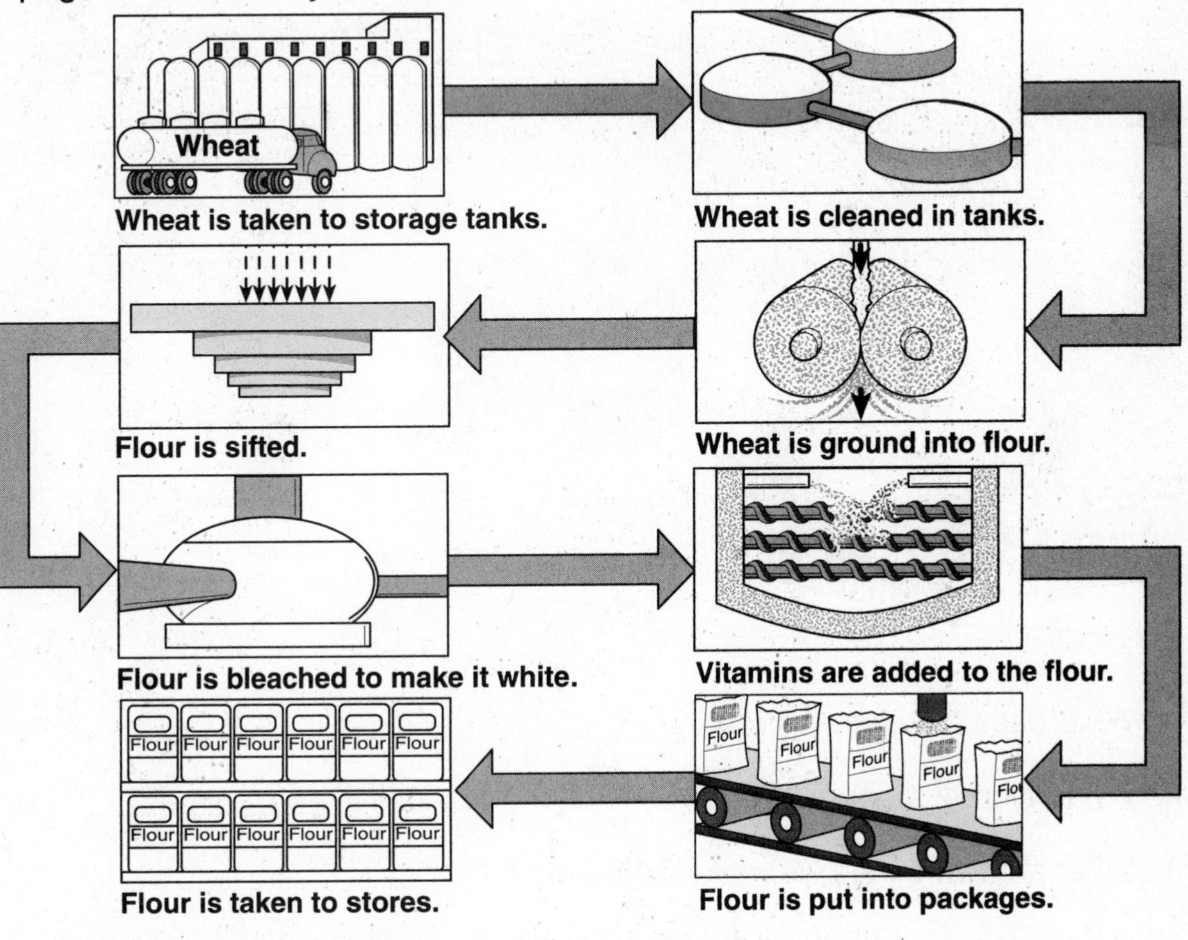

1. What is the first step in the flow chart?

____

2. Which of these steps comes first? Circle your answer.

   Wheat is ground into flour. Wheat is cleaned.

3. What happens to the flour right after it is sifted?

____

4. What happens to the flour just before it is put into packages?

____

Name: Use with pages 308–311.

THINKING ABOUT MINERAL RESOURCES

Look at the picture. Then answer the questions that follow. For help, you can look back at pages 308–311 in your textbook.

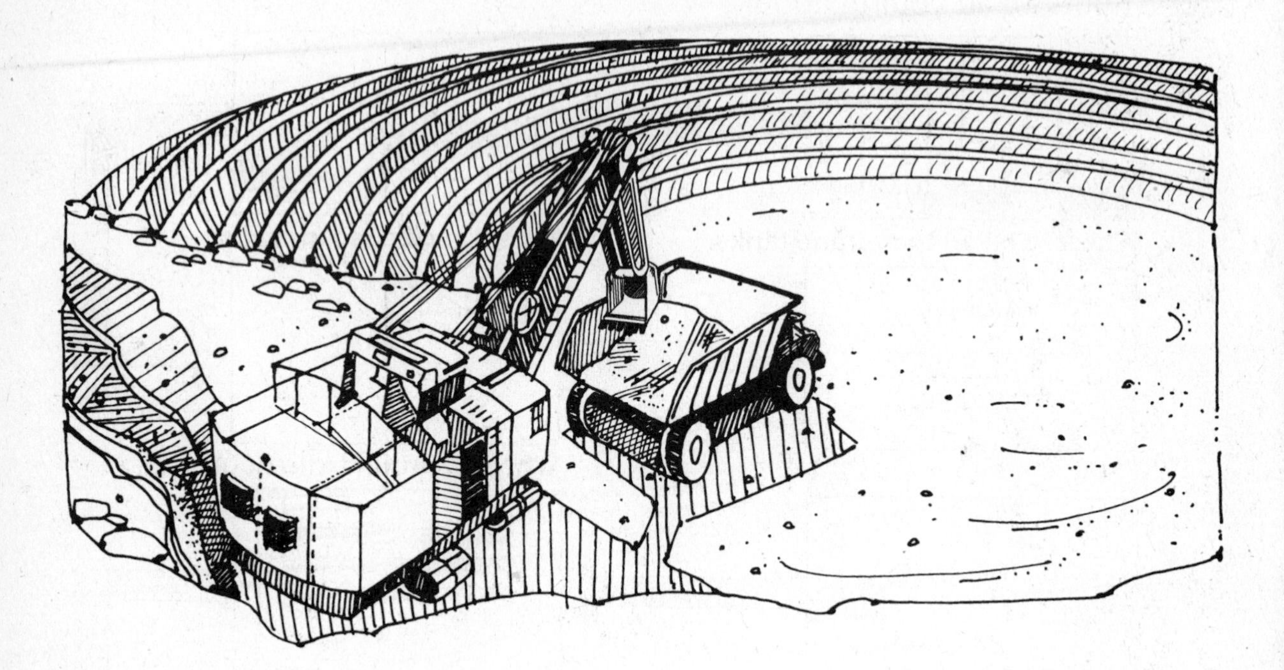

1. What does the picture show? ____________________

2. What mineral resource is being mined in the picture? ____________________

3. What are two things we make with copper? ____________________

4. Is copper a renewable or nonrenewable resource? Explain your answer.

____

____

5. List three other mineral resources that people remove from the land.

____

6. Why is it important to use all natural resources carefully?

____

____

Thinking About Manufacturing

Name the product in each picture. Tell how it is manufactured. Then answer the questions below. For help, you can look back at pages 312–318 in your textbook.

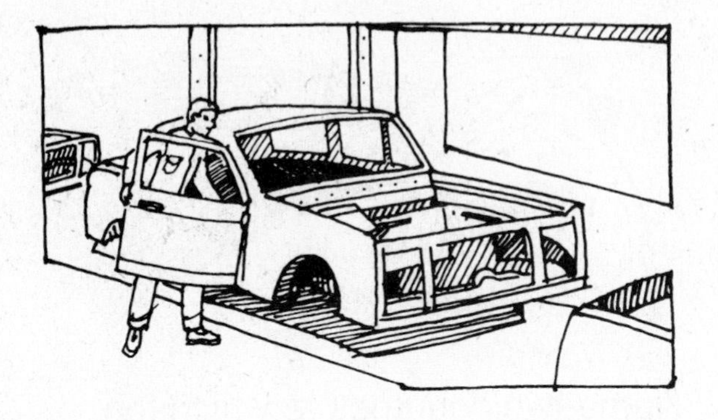

Product: ______________________

How is it manufactured?

____

____

Product: ______________________

How is it manufactured?

____

____

Name another product. Then tell how it is manufactured.

____

____

Why do you think manufacturing is one of the most important types of businesses in our country?

____

____

____

____

Name: Use with pages 320–323.

EXPORTS AND IMPORTS

Look at the pictures and follow the directions. For help, you can look back at pages 320–323 in your textbook.

Name a country to which the United States exports these products.

____

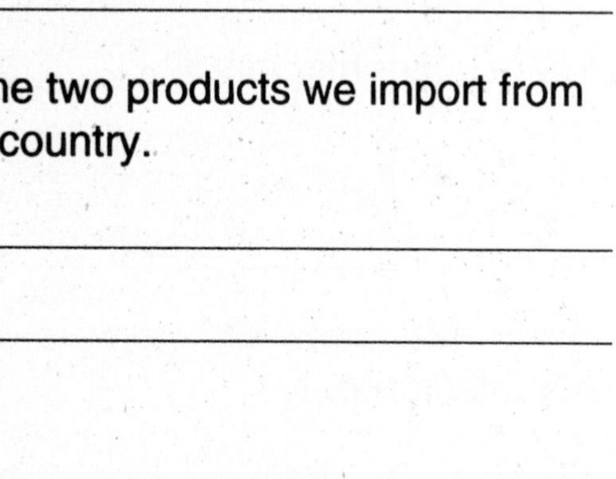

Name two products we import from this country.

____

____

Name two countries to which the United States exports this product.

____

____

Name a state in which this product is grown.

____

Name two countries from which the United States imports this product.

____

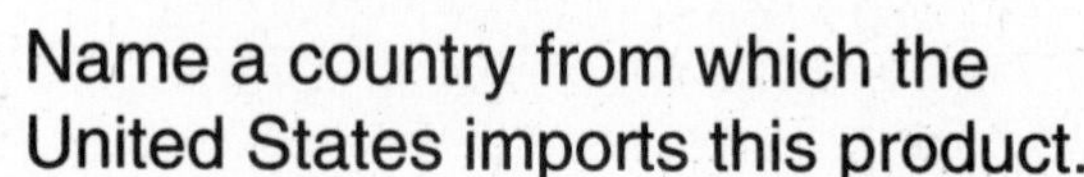

Name a country from which the United States imports this product.

____

Matching Words and Their Meanings

Write the letter of each word or term next to its meaning. For help, you can look back at the lessons in Chapter 12 of your textbook.

a. mill	**f.** renewable resource	**k.** product map	**p.** harvest
b. robot	**g.** private property	**l.** manufacturing	**q.** fertilizer
c. import	**h.** nonrenewable resource	**m.** assembly line	**r.** process
d. trade	**i.** international trade	**n.** domestic trade	**s.** factory
e. export	**j.** public property	**o.** agriculture	

_____ **1.** the business of growing crops and raising animals

_____ **2.** crops that are gathered when ripe

_____ **3.** chemicals that are used to help plants grow

_____ **4.** a map that shows the places where goods are made or grown

_____ **5.** to change something into a different form

_____ **6.** a resource that can be replaced by nature, if used carefully

_____ **7.** the business of making things

_____ **8.** land that has been set aside for all people to use

_____ **9.** a resource that cannot be replaced

_____ **10.** trade within a country

_____ **11.** a place where things are manufactured

_____ **12.** a line of workers and machines all working together to make a final product

_____ **13.** land that is owned by people or companies

_____ **14.** a machine made to do a task

_____ **15.** to sell goods to another country

_____ **16.** the buying and selling of goods and services

_____ **17.** a place where people use machines to make natural resources into finished products

_____ **18.** to buy goods from another country

_____ **19.** importing and exporting with other countries

THE GEOGRAPHY OF YOUR COMMUNITY

Write the name of your community and the name of your state. Then complete the activities. A reference book, such as an almanac, may help you.

My Community: ____________ **My State:** ____________

1. What is the population of your community? ____________

   Is your community a city, a suburb, or a town? ____________

2. How would you describe where in your state your community is located?

   ____

   ____

3. What are the important landforms in your area? ____________

   ____

   ____

4. What are the important bodies of water? ____________

   ____

   ____

5. How would you describe the climate in your area? ____________

   ____

   ____

6. List one or more natural resources in your area.

   ____________ ____________

   ____________ ____________

7. List one or more facts that make your community special.

   ____

A Song About the Environment

Make up a song about helping the environment in your community. Write words to a tune you already know. Here's a cleanup song written to the tune of "The Farmer in the Dell." You can use the same tune if you wish.

Don't Litter

Don't throw your litter here.
Don't throw your litter there.
Just put your trash where it belongs,
And do your share!

KEEP OUR TOWN CLEAN

Title ______________________________

To the tune of ______________________________

By ______________________________

____

____

____

____

____

____

____

____

Name: Use with pages 328–336.

A NEIGHBORHOOD MAP

Use the blank map below to show the neighborhood around your school. Label the streets. Use symbols to show where bus stops and other important places are located. Color the map. Don't forget to include a map key.

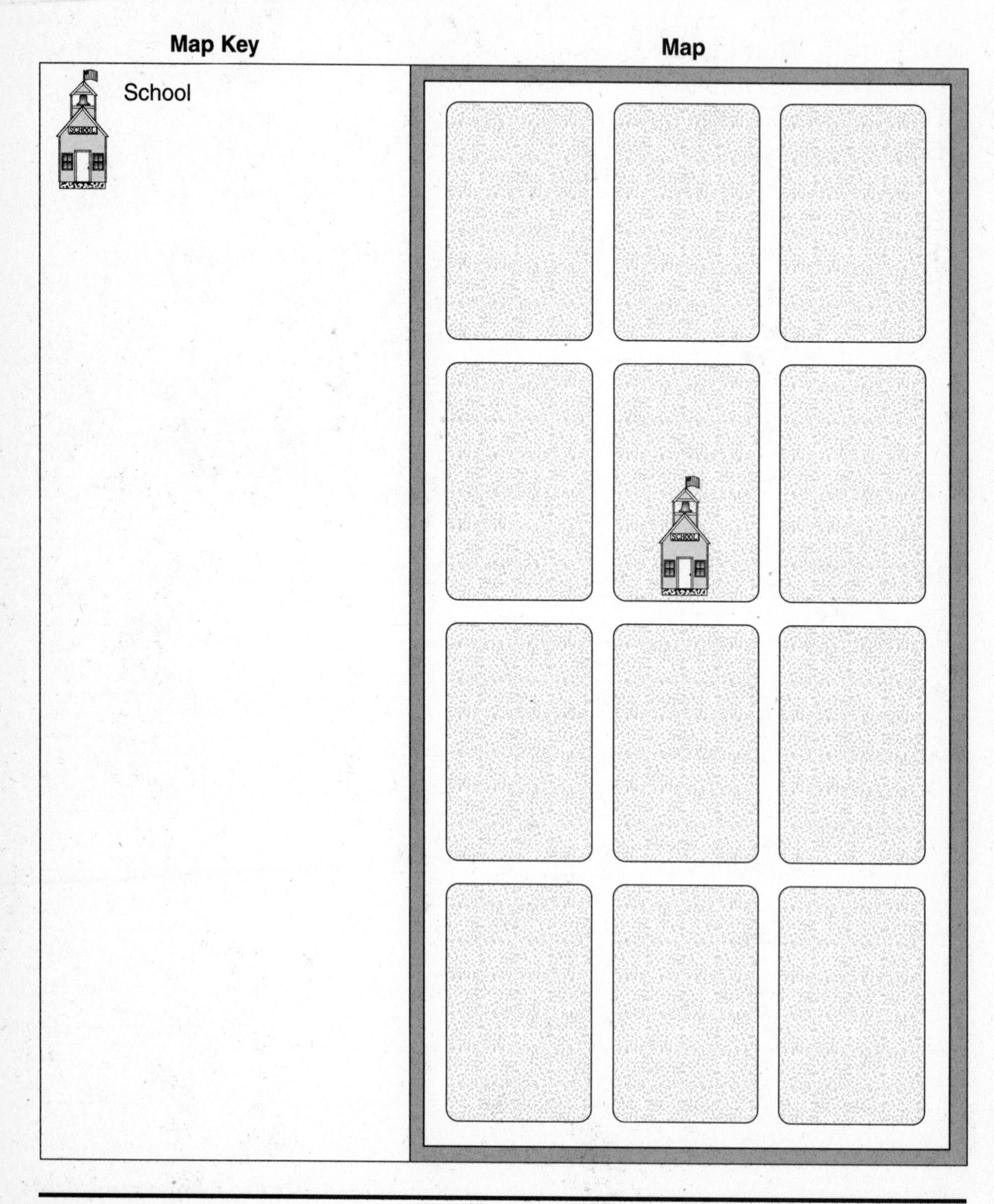

A Community Game

Make a Community Facts game. Play it with a friend.

What to Do

1. Write a question about your community on each card below.
2. Write the answer to each question in the answer box.
3. Cut out the cards.

How to Play

1. Exchange cards with a partner.
2. Take turns reading questions and giving answers.
3. You get ten points for each right answer. The person with the most points wins!

Questions About Your Community

Question 1: ____________________

____

____

Question 2: ____________________

____

____

Question 3: ____________________

____

____

Question 4: ____________________

____

____

Answer Box

1. ____________________

2. ____________________

3. ____________________

4. ____________________